DIGITAL
STORAGE SYSTEMS

DIGITAL STORAGE SYSTEMS

WILLIAM RENWICK

M.A., B.Sc., M.Brit.I.R.E., A.M.I.E.E.
Chief Engineer, Basic and Digital Research,
Plessey Co. (U.K.) Ltd.

LONDON
E. & F. N. SPON LTD.
22 Henrietta Street, W.C.2
1964

PREFACE

Of all the component parts of a digital computer, the characteristics of the store play a most important part in determining the characteristics of the complete system. Only when suitable forms of store became available at the end of World War II, did the computer, as first envisaged by Babbage over a century ago, become a reality. Modern computers and data-processing systems were made possible by developments in digital storage and these developments are also finding widespread application in many branches of science and engineering. The inspiration of this book lay in a feeling that the subject had never received the treatment which its importance warranted. Although other areas of application are mentioned where appropriate, the types of store are discussed with reference to their use in the digital-computer field, which has stimulated most of the research and development as well as providing the bulk of the applications.

The book has been written primarily as a guide for the designer of any system employing digital techniques, firstly to guide him in his choice of store for differing applications and, secondly, to give him an appreciation of the problems which confront the engineer designing storage systems. It is not meant to be a design text-book although I hope it will be of value to the designer in clarifying the fundamental principles underlying all digital storage systems. The references and bibliography will help the reader who wants a more detailed discussion of the design of any system. A minimum basic knowledge of the design of digital systems is assumed, so that the engineer new to the field should have little difficulty in following the discussion.

In addition to the many storage systems which are in present use (and which are reviewed in the last chapter), some are included which are now obsolete for most applications but which are of historical importance. New methods which are not yet fully developed, but which show promise of important advantages, are also described.

Acknowledgement is due to all the scientists and engineers on whose work are based the advances described. I wish also to record my gratitude to my colleagues past and present, especially to Mr. F. G. Jenks who read the manuscript and made many helpful comments and suggestions.

W. Renwick

August, 1963

CONTENTS

ACCESS, DIGIT AND CONTROL CIRCUITS IN
RANDOM-ACCESS SYSTEMS

REVIEW OF CURRENT AND FUTURE
DEVELOPMENTS

CHAPTER 1

INTRODUCTION

ONE of the most important functions needed in the organization of a data-processing system is data storage. The concept of the modern general-purpose computing machine depends on the availability of a unit to store both data and, just as important, the programme of instructions which enables the computer to carry out the calculation at high speed without the intervention of the operator. Although its major application is in computers, due to the increasing use of digital methods in other branches of electronic engineering, the need for digital-data storage is becoming widespread. One important application outside the computing field is in the electronic telephone exchange, where a variety of storage techniques is being employed. In many scientific experiments the results are now recorded (or stored) in digital form and the large amount of data is later processed and reduced in a computer. Digital-data transmission is another field in which storage is required, if optimum use is made of the channel capacity and if error-detecting and correcting systems are employed. The explosive rate at which technical information is now being generated has led to an increasing interest in the mechanization of information retrieval systems. The digital computer has an important part to play in this mechanization but its contribution to the solution of the problem depends on the availability of mass storage at low cost. Since the stimulus behind the research and development into storage techniques has, so far, mainly come from the computer field, the various storage mechanisms will be discussed with particular reference to their application in digital computers, although other applications will be mentioned where appropriate.

The store or memory, as it is often called, in a digital computer must be *erasable* and *accessible*; the first infers that the store can

1

be erased and re-used, while the second indicates that items of information can be located in the store and extracted, or that new items can be inserted in the correct place. The item of information which is normally processed is known as a *word*; this may represent either a number or the coded form of an instruction to the computer. The total storage, or *capacity*, is divided into *locations*, each of which contains one word and is specified by an *address*; this is a number, or code, which enables the store-access system to find the correct location. The capacity of a system is usually measured by the total number of binary digits, or bits, which can be stored or by the number of words each of so many binary digits, *e.g.* 3200 bits or 128 words of 25 bits. Two times measure the speed of operation of a storage system, the *access time* and the *access-cycle time* or *cycle time*; the access time is the delay which occurs between the initiation of a reading operation and the time when the required information is available at the output; the access-cycle time is the minimum time between the start of successive operations. In many cases, operation of the machine is held up until the information is available from the store. A low access time is therefore an important advantage. During the remainder of the cycle, operation of the store and the computer may carry on simultaneously and cycle time may not be as important in determining the overall operating speed of the computer.

The representation of numbers in the binary scale of notation, in which only the digits 0 and 1 can occur, has many advantages in the realization of a computer. Many of the elements of which a digital system is constructed have two distinct states; *e.g.* an electromagnetic relay is either on or off, a switch is either open or closed, and an electronic valve, operated as a switch, is either passing a current or not, a card or tape may either have a hole punched or not. Where elements are capable of more than two states, it is still advantageous, in the interests of reliability, to limit their operation to two states only, since obviously the discrimination between these is enhanced; *e.g.* it is quite possible to use ten distinct voltage levels on one wire to represent the ten decimal digits but, if the two extreme levels are chosen to represent the two binary digits, the system is very much less liable to errors due to ambiguity in interpreting the voltage level received. The use of two-state elements does not make the binary scale of notation obligatory, since decimal numbers can be coded with a set of such elements. Probably the simplest coding is the one-out-of-ten code in which each decimal digit is represented by turning on only one element from a set of ten. This code, however, has a high redundancy since the ten elements could represent numbers up to $2^{10} - 1$ (or 1023), the equivalent of over three decimal digits. If two-state elements are employed the use of the binary notation thus simplifies the design of the machine and reduces the amount of equipment required. Most storage systems share this two-state characteristic; *e.g.* a ferromagnet has two remanent states, current can flow in two directions in a super-conductor, and an element with a negative resistance characteristic, such as a tunnel diode, with the correct bias, has two stable operating points. Again those elements with more than two possible states have a higher degree of reliability when limited to binary operation.

1.1 HISTORICAL

Charles Babbage, who was Lucasion Professor of Mathematics at Cambridge from 1828 to 1839, in his plans for the Analytic Engine, divided it into three parts—the mill, or what is now called the arithmetic unit, a unit which would now be called the control unit and the store. It is interesting to note that Babbage planned the store of the engine to have a capacity of 1000 numbers each of 50 decimal digits, or the equivalent of some 2×10^5 binary digits; only in recent years have machines with capacities in this range become common. The history of electronic digital computers has been intimately bound up with the development of suitable storage mechanisms, and the exploitation of improvements in the operating speed of circuits depends on the availability of stores with matching improvements in their characteristics. When it is remembered that the store of Babbage's engine was to consist of mechanical counting wheels, it is not surprising that the machine was never built. The realization of such a machine had to wait for the advances in electronics which have been made in the last two decades.

The ENIAC, completed at the Moore School of Electrical Engineering in the University of Pennsylvania during World War II, was the first electronic digital computer, but had provision for the storage of only twenty numbers, each of ten decimal digits.

The first stored-programme machines were made possible by the development, between 1945 and 1950, of the ultrasonic acoustic-delay-line store, the magnetic drum and various electrostatic storage tubes. The acoustic-delay line had been developed towards the end of the 1939–45 World War, for use in sophisticated radar systems. Recording on a magnetic surface had been used for sound recording on wire or tape and it was a comparatively straightforward step to put the magnetic material on the surface of a continuously rotating cylinder. Considerable effort went into the development of several different forms of electrostatic storage tubes; one of the most successful of these was the cathode-ray-tube store invented by F. C. Williams and T. Kilburn at Manchester University.

The design of the first generation of electronic computers in the years before 1950 was influenced to a great extent by the characteristics of the storage mechanisms then available. Access to most of these stores was *sequential*, in that access to a location could only be obtained by scanning through all the intervening locations; this lent itself to the design of computers operating in the *serial* mode, in which the digits of a number follow one another successively on a single channel. During this period, serial binary computers, like the EDVAC designed at the Moore School of Electrical Engineering in the University of Pennsylvania, the EDSAC built at the University Mathematical Laboratory, Cambridge, and the pilot ACE designed and built at the National Physical Laboratory, all incorporated acoustic-delay lines. Other serial computers of this period included the Manchester University computer designed at the Electrical Engineering Laboratory, which employed the Williams C.R.T. store, the APEX.C designed by Booth at Birkbeck College, London University and the MARK III at Harvard University both of which made use of magnetic drums for storage. Based on these early machines came the first commercial developments in the early 1950s; UNIVAC, designed by Eckert and Mauchly, the designers of the ENIAC, employed acoustic-delay lines. LEO built by J. Lyons and Co. was based on the EDSAC, the English Electric Co.'s DEUCE was based on the pilot ACE and the Ferranti MARK I was based on the machine at Manchester University.

The first binary machine operating in the *parallel* mode, in which the digits of a number appear simultaneously on separate channels, made use of electrostatic storage tubes for the internal store. WHIRLWIND I, designed and built at the Massachusetts Institute of Technology, used a specially designed storage tube. In England, at T.R.E., Malvern, a parallel machine was constructed with a Williams C.R.T. store operating in a parallel fashion. This type of store was also adopted for the machine built at the Institute of Advanced Study, Princeton, New Jersey; several other machines, such as the ILLIAC at the University of Illinois and the MANIAC I, at Los Alamos, New Mexico, were based on this machine. Although these and several other similar machines, including the IBM 701, were put into operation, the reliability of the electrostatic tubes left a lot to be desired. The attempts to find an alternative were successful at MIT where the rectangular-hysteresis loop ferrite core was developed, leading to the replacement of the electrostatic store in WHIRLWIND by a ferrite-core store in 1953.

The introduction of the ferrite core marked a significant point in the development of storage systems and of digital computers. Previously the more successful high-speed storage systems had been sequential-access systems using continuous media. The ferrite core made the large-scale use of a discrete element for the storage of each binary digit economical and made possible *random-access* systems in which the access time is independent of the location of the information in the store. In addition to making random access possible, the ferrite core has other advantages; whereas the electrostatic storage tube and the acoustic-delay line are *volatile* types of storage in which the information stored is destroyed when the power supplies are switched off, this need not be the case with the ferrite core. The reliability of the ferrite-core stores proved to be much higher than previous high-speed storage mechanisms, which were soon made obsolete and gradually replaced in all major computer developments. The use of magnetic drums continued in the smaller computers because of their lower cost, but the reduction in price of the ferrite core has now led to the adoption of core stores for even the smaller computers. The magnetic drum, of course, is still used in many computing systems as a larger-capacity backing store associated with a lower-capacity core store. Improvements in ferrite materials and the development of new techniques has led to a considerable increase in the operating speed of core stores during the last few years.

The bulk storage of information was solved in the early machines by the use of punched paper tape or punched cards, but the long access time and the space required were severe drawbacks to their use. The development of magnetic tape, which had been considered as an input and output mechanism for the EDVAC as early as 1944, resolved some of these difficulties. The sequential access to information stored on magnetic tape was still a severe drawback and many systems based on magnetic surface recording have now been developed which have partial random access to very large quantities of information. Systems based on several tape loops, flexible or rigid magnetic discs and magnetic cards are now available with a maximum capacity up to some 10^9 bits and with access times as low as 0·1 second.

Research and development in the field of storage systems continue on an increasing scale. The emphasis in this work is directed towards increased capacity and operating speed and decrease in cost. The most promising developments, which may replace the ferrite-core store in the future, are based on thin, flat, ferromagnetic films and superconducting films. Small magnetic-film stores are already in operation in one or two computers; the Remington Rand UNIVAC 1107 is the first commercially available machine with such a store, although the capacity and speed of the magnetic-film unit is very modest. The superconducting store suffers from the disadvantage of requiring a liquid-helium refrigerator but this may be outweighed by its advantage of increased capacity combined with increased operating speed.

The limit which is set by the physical dimensions of elements and the length of the interconnections is likely to be a more decisive factor than their intrinsic switching speed in determining the ultimate speed of a storage system; techniques which promise a significant reduction in the size of the element and a corresponding increase in the packing density are therefore essential. A reduction in the dimensions of the individual element has the added advantage of reducing the required driving power, since the energy dissipated is usually proportional to the volume of material which is switched.

1.2 ORGANIZATION OF A TYPICAL STORAGE UNIT

The principal parts of a typical storage unit are shown in Fig. 1.1. These are the access or selection circuits, the digit circuits, the storage medium and the control unit. When an initiate 'read' signal is received by the control unit, the access circuits select the location specified by the address input and the information stored in the location is made available via the digit circuits at the output. When a 'write' signal is received, the input information is stored in the location specified by the address. The form of the access and digit circuits depends on the type of store, especially on whether it is a parallel or serial system. In a parallel system as many digit circuits are required as there are digits in the word, while in a serial system only one digit circuit is required. The store control unit generates the waveforms necessary for the correct

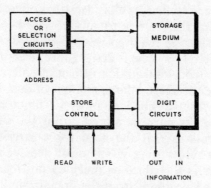

FIG. 1.1 *Parts of a typical storage unit*

operation of the store, when stimulated by an external read or write signal. In addition, control signals can be made available to the rest of the system of which the store forms part; these signals facilitate the synchronization and make possible the simultaneous operation of the store and of the rest of the system.

The major problem with all storage systems is not in the storage of information but in obtaining access to it. When time is one of the selection coordinates, as in a serial or sequential-access system, this problem is greatly simplified. As the number of digits stored per channel increases, the cost of the access circuits, expressed in terms of the cost per digit stored, is reduced; unfortunately there is always a minimum time interval which can be allotted to one digit, so that an increase in the number of digits stored in one channel leads inevitably to an increase in the access time. With random-access systems, unless the storage element

B

itself can perform part of the selection process, like the rectangular-loop ferrite core, for example, the access circuits can become large and costly.

1.3 STORAGE REQUIREMENTS IN DIGITAL COMPUTERS

While it is certainly convenient for the computer programmer to have only one level of random-access store, this will almost certainly be ruled out by the restrictions imposed by the physical size of the store as well as by considerations of cost. To overcome these restrictions the store is usually arranged in several levels, each meeting differing requirements which depend on the applications for which the system is designed. In scientific calculations, such as the numerical integration of partial differential equations of two or more variables, a large amount of data is generated by the computer from a small quantity of input data and these intermediate results must be stored during the calculation. It is in such applications that the need for a large-capacity, high-speed, random-access store is felt most keenly; the aim of the logical designer is to reduce as much as possible the effects on programming which result from the organization of the store in several levels. Figure 1.2 is a block schematic of the organization of the store in such a machine. In this example, the store is arranged in three levels, the main store from which all the operations are carried out, the backing store and the auxiliary store. If block transfers can take place automatically between the main and backing stores the system can be used as if it were a random-access store with a capacity equal to the combined capacities of the two levels. The auxiliary store serves as a very large-capacity store with longer access time.

Also shown in Fig. 1.2 is the index, or modifier number, store which is part of the machine control unit; this has the requirements of high-speed operation with a restricted capacity. Access to this store is required as a stage in the execution of an instruction, so that the access time must only be a fraction of the cycle time of the main store, if the operation of the machine is not to be slowed down unduly. The number of modifier registers varies from machine to machine but is usually not more than 128.

Increasingly, permanent storage methods are being employed

in computers to store fixed information, such as frequently used sub-routines and constants, and to increase the facilities which the machine offers, by effectively extending the instruction code. Because the reading operation only is required, the cycle time is low. Capacities required normally lie between 1000 and 4000 words. When instructions are executed from the fixed store, some

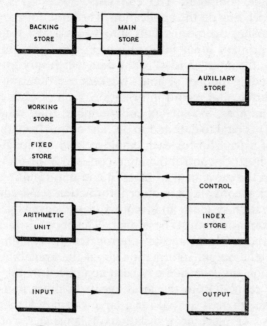

FIG. 1.2 *Organization of a scientific computer showing various stores*

erasable storage is required to hold intermediate results during the calculation. It is convenient that this should be separate from the main store and the block of storage labelled working store in Fig. 1.2, is used for this purpose. The access time should be less than that of the main store with as short a cycle time as possible. The capacity required is normally less than 1000 words.

Small 'buffer' storage units may be associated with input and output mechanisms and with auxiliary storage units to simplify the transfer of information to and from the computer. These must be capable of operating in synchronism with the central computer or the external unit. For example, during the transfer of information from a magnetic drum to an output printer, the data are first transferred at the drum transfer rate to the buffer store, from which they are available for transfer to the printer at the output rate.

Storage requirements for data-processing systems, or computers for business applications, fall into similar categories to those in the scientific computer. The emphasis, however, is differently placed, depending on the application. The input for most business data-processing operations falls into two classes, record or file data and primary input information. For example, in a payroll calculation the input consists of the data which vary from week to week, including number of hours worked, overtime and so on, for each employee, and record information, such as each employee's reference number, income-tax code number, total wages paid to date, total tax paid to date and so on. The output from the machine consists of a pay-slip for each employee and an updated record. Similarly, in stock control the input consists of the previous stock record and the movement of parts in and out, resulting in an updated stock record and any other information required. In airline seat-reservation systems, an inventory of seats available and flight status information must be stored. The input from any of a large number of local agents interrogates the equipment which then transmits output information about the availability of seats, an indication that the sale has been completed or the answer to any other request from the local agent. In other non-numerical applications, there is a need for a large-capacity file store which, in the case of machine translation of languages, for example, contains a dictionary of word stems.

Figure 1.3 shows the organization of a typical data-processing system. The central processor is essentially a digital computer with its own internal store of limited capacity. External storage of two types may be provided, the file store and a group of auxiliary storage units from which off-line input and output mechanisms can be operated if required. When the record information can be dealt with sequentially and always in the same order, for example, in payroll and stock inventory applications, random access to the record is not required. However, in file applications such as machine translation or seat-reservation systems, where there is no order in the requests to the file, a random-access system reduces the waiting time after an interrogation. For applications of this type, the need arises for a large-capacity random-access file store,

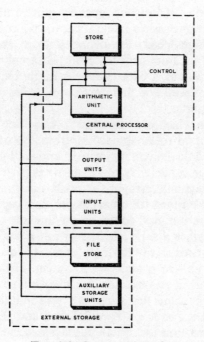

FIG. 1.3 *Organization of a data-processing system*

which has a capacity greater than 10^8 bits and as short an access time as possible.

1.4 CLASSIFICATION OF STORAGE SYSTEMS

Storage systems can be classified according to their use in a computer or data-processing system as internal, including main and backing stores, and external or auxiliary. They can also be classified according to their major characteristics, for example, as erasable, semipermanent or permanent, volatile or non-volatile and random, sequential or random-sequential access (in which the access is partly random and partly sequential). In addition they can be subject to a less specific or more relative classification according to access time and capacity; high-speed, low-capacity, medium-speed, medium-capacity and low-speed, large-capacity systems. These classifications overlap and the characteristics which are most useful to the designer depend a great deal on the application. Internal storage is an integral part of the computer and may consist of a high-speed, low-capacity store backed up by a medium-speed, medium-capacity unit. External storage, on the other hand, is usually a bulk storage medium capable of holding large amounts of data and therefore mainly consists of low-speed, large-capacity units.

Any numbers which are allocated to the three capacity classifications are bound to be somewhat arbitrary, but the following divisions do include the vast majority of applications in the various categories. Large-capacity systems can be taken to include everything with a capacity greater than 10^7 binary digits; medium capacity from 10^5 up to 10^7 binary digits; low capacity below 10^5. The allocation of numbers to the access-time classification is even more arbitrary since a store which may serve as a high-speed unit in a medium-speed computer, say, may be classed only as a medium-speed unit in a high-speed system. However, it is convenient to classify access times in the following speed ranges: low-speed includes all access times greater than 1 millisecond; medium-speed access times between 1 millisecond and 10 microseconds; high-speed access times less than 10 microseconds. As reductions in access time become possible, it may be necessary to introduce a fourth class of very high speed with access times less than 0.1 microsecond.

In the chapters which follow, various methods of storage are considered in detail, but less space is devoted to those systems which are now mainly of historical interest. The physical basis of these storage systems is described and the methods of obtaining access to the stored information are discussed. Since they are similar for all random-access systems and are of considerable importance, the principles governing access to a store consisting of discrete storage elements are treated separately in Chapter 9. New developments which appear to offer improvements of significance to the system designer, although development is not complete, are discussed in some detail. The final chapter includes a general review of storage systems with descriptions and specifications of systems which are available to meet the requirements in various applications, together with an assessment of future possibilities and ultimate limitations in speed and capacity.

BIBLIOGRAPHY

1. *Charles Babbage and his Calculating Engines.* Selected writings by Charles Babbage and others. Edited by Philip Morrison and Emily Morrison. Dover Publications, Inc. (New York, 1961).

2. Wilkes, M. V. *Automatic Digital Computers.* Methuen and Co. (London, 1956).

3. Alt, Franz L. *Electronic Digital Computers. (Their use in Science and Engineering.)* Academic Press (New York, 1958).

4. Richards, R. K. *Digital Computer Components and Circuits.* D. Van Nostrand Company (Princeton, New Jersey, 1957).

5. Grabbe, E. M., Ramo, S. and Wooldridge, D. E. *Handbook of Automation, Computation and Control.* 2, 'Computers and Data Processing'. John Wiley and Sons (New York, 1959).

CHAPTER 2

DELAY LINE STORAGE

ANY medium with propagation delay can be used for digital storage, as illustrated in Fig. 2.1. If a signal, representing a binary digit, is introduced at the input of the delay medium, after the elapse of a time equal to the delay, it will appear at the output.

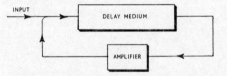

FIG. 2.1 *Principle of delay-line storage*

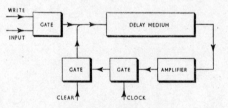

FIG. 2.2 *Block diagram of delay-line store*

After amplification, in principle it can be fed back to the input and so continue to circulate indefinitely. If the delay time is equal to many *digit periods* (that is, the time allocated to a single digit), a serial stream of digits, occupying a period of time equal to the delay, can be introduced at the input. These digits will then continue to circulate continuously and the information they represent will be stored as long as the power is turned on. Because of bandwidth limitations and phase distortion in the medium and amplifier, the signal suffers attenuation and distortion so that it

14

would be lost after several passages through the delay and amplifier. To overcome this limitation, the system of Fig. 2.2 is used in which the output signal is not applied directly to the input but to a gate, which then allows an undistorted and re-timed pulse from a continuously running clock-pulse generator to pass to the input. The input signal is then independent of the number of times the

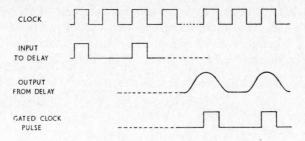

FIG. 2.3 *Waveforms in delay-line store*

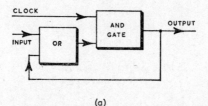

(a)

FIG. 2.4(a) *Regenerative clock-pulse gate*

information has circulated through the medium so that the storage time is indefinite. Typical waveforms illustrating the operation of the system are shown in Fig. 2.3. Unwanted information can be cleared from the store by inhibiting the signal applied to the clear gate, which is always open in normal operation. To write into the store the 'clear' gate is closed and the 'write' gate opened, thus allowing new information to pass to the delay line. The tolerance of this clock-pulse gating system to timing variations can obviously be increased by reducing the width of the clock-pulse so that the output from the amplifier is sampled for a short time only. The output of the clock-pulse gate can now be lengthened before applying it to the input of the delay line. Figure 2.4(a) shows a simple method for achieving this. As long as the input pulse overlaps the leading edge of a clock-pulse the regenerative action of the feedback path will make the output a complete clock-pulse as illustrated by the waveforms of Fig. 2.4(b).

In the interests of economy, the circuits associated with one delay unit should deal with as many digits as possible. However, for a fixed digit period, the number of digits stored is proportional to the delay time, so that the maximum access time, which is equal to the delay time, increases with capacity. The choice of capacity, therefore, is a compromise between cost and access time. The desirable characteristics of the delay medium are low

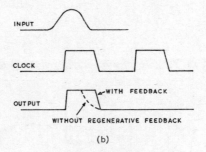

(b)

FIG. 2.4(b) *Waveforms for regenerative gate*

attenuation and low dispersion, wide bandwidth and low-propagation velocity. Since the delay line functions as a communication channel, the results of Information or Communication Theory apply. A well-known theorem states that the amount of information which can be transmitted per second, or channel capacity, is proportional to the channel bandwidth. The amount of information which can be stored in a delay line, or storage capacity, is therefore also proportional to the bandwidth. A high value of delay per unit length or low velocity of propagation in the medium reduces the physical dimensions of the store, while the lower the attenuation of the line, the less amplification is required in the loop and the lower the cost of the regeneration circuits.

Although either distributed or lumped parameter electromagnetic delay lines can be used for storage, their high propagation velocity limits their use to applications where a short delay or low capacity is required.[1,2] The velocity of sound in any medium is very low compared with the velocity of propagation of electromagnetic radiation, so that the utilization of the transmission delay of sound waves is attractive for larger-capacity storage systems. An acoustic delay line consists of the essential parts shown in Fig. 2.5. The electrical input energy is transformed by the input transducer to acoustic energy, which propagates through the delay medium with the velocity of sound to the output transducer, where the acoustic energy is converted back to the electrical output signal. Liquid media have the following advantages compared with solids. Firstly, the velocity of sound in a solid is several times the velocity in a liquid, so that the path length for a given delay is less in a liquid. Secondly, sound can

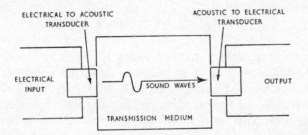

FIG. 2.5 *Essential parts of an acoustic delay line*

only be propagated as a compressional or longitudinal wave in a liquid but, in a solid, both transverse and longitudinal waves can be propagated with different velocities. Care must therefore be taken in design to avoid setting up alternative modes by reflection or refraction, since they may lead to unwanted transmission paths giving rise to spurious outputs from the delay line. When the transverse dimensions, or dimensions at right angles to the direction of propagation, are comparable with the wavelength being transmitted, severe dispersion can occur due to intermode coupling by Poisson contraction effects. This dispersion can be avoided by making the transverse dimensions much greater than the wavelength, although it is also possible to use the compressional mode when these dimensions are much less than a wavelength. The use of torsional waves in a rod with a circular cross-section has the advantage that no dispersion occurs at any diameter.

Water has been used as the transmission medium but the most

successful units with a liquid medium have employed mercury. Fused-quartz, solid, delay units have also been built, in which multiple internal reflections were used to reduce the volume required to contain a given transmission delay. Solid media have also been used in the form of thin wire which can be coiled to reduce the space occupied. Transducers based on the piezoelectric effect in a quartz crystal and on the magnetostrictive effect in a magnetic material have been used. While fused-quartz delay lines have never been incorporated in a digital computer, mercury units have been widely used. Magnetostrictive delay lines, in addition to their use in several medium-size computers, have more recently been applied in electronic telephone switching systems.

2.1 MERCURY DELAY LINES

The first acoustic storage systems to be incorporated in a digital computer employed mercury delay lines in which the transducers were X-cut quartz crystals.[3,4] Figure 2.6 shows a sectional view of a typical mercury delay line. When an alternating voltage is applied across the transmitting crystal between the mercury and the back electrode, due to the piezo-electric effect, the crystal vibrates at the input frequency. These vibrations are transmitted to the mercury in contact with the crystal and propagate down the column to the receiving crystal, where the reverse process takes place, resulting in an electrical signal from the output terminals. For wide bandwidth, it is essential that the crystals should be heavily loaded by the transmission medium. Since the acoustic impedance of mercury is a good match to that of quartz, the intrinsic bandwidth is of the order of 25 to 50 per cent of the centre frequency. An incidental advantage of mercury as the medium is the ease with which the electrical signal can be applied to the quartz crystal, since it is a conductor of electricity. To reduce the effects of frequency dispersion or phase distortion and the variation of attenuation with frequency, best results are obtained when the signal is modulated on to a carrier lying between 10 and 20 Mc/s. The attenuation in a mercury delay line is made up of two parts; the loss due to the transducers is the major part and may be as high as 50 db; the attenuation in the mercury itself increases as the square of the frequency and is 1·2 db per ft (·04 db per cm) at 10 Mc/s.

When the acoustic wave impinges on the receiving crystal, some energy is reflected back to the transmitting crystal where it is again reflected to the receiver. This twice-reflected signal may give rise to spurious outputs if the attenuation in the mercury is low and the reflection coefficient is high. In long delay lines the transmission attenuation is great enough to reduce the reflected signal to a level where it does not cause any trouble but in units with a short transmission path steps must be taken to eliminate these signals. One solution is obtained by backing the crystals with a material which presents a good acoustic match to mercury; in some units mercury itself has been used. When the transmitted energy reaches the receiving crystal no reflection takes place,

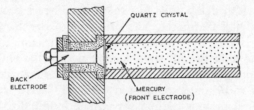

FIG. 2.6 *Section through mercury delay line*

since the crystal is exactly half a wavelength in thickness, and the energy passes into the backing material where it is scattered by an irregular reflecting surface.[3] Another solution is the introduction of some extra attenuation in the transmission path which decreases the amplitude of the reflected signals in relation to the direct signals.[4] This latter solution makes the use of a dry back electrode possible, giving nearly complete reflection of the incident wave since an almost perfect mismatch is caused by the thin film of air between the crystal and the back electrode. With this type of electrode, the attenuation of the line is decreased by 6 db, that is, 3 db at each crystal. Units consisting of several transmission paths in one mercury bath have been constructed.[5] These rely on the directional effect of the quartz transducer which only radiates a narrow beam when its diameter is much greater than the wavelength.

Since the velocity of sound in mercury is approximately 475 ft per sec ($1\cdot45 \times 10^5$ cm per sec), a delay of 1 millisecond requires a path length of some 57 in. (145 cm). The physical size of the delay line, therefore, restricts the maximum delay to about 1 millisecond. In addition to the bandwidth restriction, the number of digits which may be stored in one unit is limited by the effect of temperature variations (see Section 2.4). Mercury delay lines have been constructed with capacities of up to 1000 bits at digit frequencies of several Mc/s.

2.2   QUARTZ DELAY LINES

In applications where vibration may occur or where small size and light weight are required, the mercury delay line is at a severe disadvantage and the use of a solid medium offers advantages. Fused quartz, whose acoustic impedance is an almost perfect match to a quartz crystal, has been successfully employed in wide bandwidth delay units but these have never been incorporated in a digital computer. The principle of construction of the quartz line is similar to the mercury line, consisting of a piece of fused quartz with quartz crystals cemented to the ends. In fused quartz the propagation velocity of the shear or transverse wave is about 4.81×10^5 cm/s, compared with 5.97×10^5 cm/s for the compressional or longitudinal wave. The longitudinal mode can be excited using X-cut crystals as in a mercury line, while Y- or AT-cut crystals can be used to excite the transverse mode. This is preferred because of its lower velocity of propagation. Even with this mode, however, the delay per unit length is less than 30 per cent of the delay in mercury; a delay time of 1 millisecond, for example, requires a path length of some $15\frac{1}{2}$ ft (4·8 m). Such a unit employing a single rod would be very difficult to fabricate, so that a folded transmission path is obligatory for delays of this order.

Units have been constructed to provide a long transmission path in a small volume by multiple reflection of the acoustic wave from the inner surfaces of a solid quartz block. The compressional mode is not suitable for multiple reflection units since it is partially or entirely converted to the transverse mode on reflection at any angle of incidence other than vertical. Care must be taken to see that the angle of incidence of the transverse wave is such that compressional waves are not set up on reflection. The design of multiple-reflection delay lines is an interesting exercise in geometry and some extremely ingenious shapes have been proposed. One of the simplest is a nearly regular polygon with an odd number of sides which can be used with the star-shaped path illustrated in Fig. 2.7 for the nonagon. In this case the polygon is regular, with the exception of the sides on which the crystals are mounted; these are machined to give the correct angle of incidence on the first reflecting surface and vertical incidence on the receiving crystal. Variations on this geometry, where more than two sides of the polygon are tilted, can result in longer transmission paths in which the beam is reflected more than once

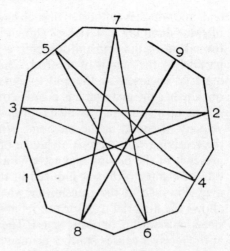

FIG. 2.7 *Multiple reflection path in nonagon*

from some of the sides. Units have been designed in which the acoustic wave follows a three-dimensional path.

Fused-quartz lines, although they offer improvements in bandwidth, attenuation, temperature coefficient of delay and robustness over the mercury line, have never been widely used because of their high initial cost. Unless the medium is very homogeneous and the reflecting surfaces machined with high accuracy, the acoustic wave will be diffracted resulting in spurious output signals.

2.3 MAGNETOSTRICTIVE DELAY LINES

Whereas other types of acoustic delay lines are named according to the delay medium used, the magnetostrictive delay line takes its name from the type of electromechanical transducer on which it is based, namely, the magnetostrictive or Joule effect in a magnetic material. If a magnetic field is applied parallel to the length of a sample of such a material, the sample will undergo a change in length. By the inverse magnetostrictive or Villari effect there is a change of flux in a sample to which a magnetic field is applied, when it is subjected to a mechanical strain. In its simplest form the magnetostrictive delay line consists of a rod of magnetostrictive material, on which two solenoids are wound, one at each end, and which is supported at each end by an acoustic termination of some damping material, as shown in Fig. 2.8. When current is turned on in the transmitting coil, a magnetic field is generated parallel to the length of the rod. This magnetic field causes the material enclosed by the coil to expand or contract, depending on whether the material has positive or negative magnetostriction, setting up a stress-pulse which is propagated along the rod with the velocity of sound in the medium. When the stress-pulse reaches the receiving coil, there is a change of flux in the rod, due to the presence of the biasing magnet, and an e.m.f. proportional to the rate of change of flux is induced in the coil. The collapse of the magnetic field at the transmitter when the current is turned off allows the material to return to its normal length and generates a stress-pulse of the opposite sense. The arrival of this second pulse at the receiver causes another change of flux and a voltage output of the opposite polarity. Typical waveforms are shown in Fig. 2.9(a). The best compromise between resolution and output voltage amplitude occurs when the duration of the input current is made equal to the time it takes the stress-pulse to travel the length of the transducer coil. The waveforms are then as shown in Fig. 2.9(b) in which the two negative voltage peaks have now combined to form one single peak of twice the amplitude. Also shown in Fig. 2.9(b) is the output waveform when successive input pulses are applied.

The maximum frequency which can be transmitted efficiently is determined by the effective length of the transducer solenoids, which is equal to half the minimum acoustic wavelength in the medium, corresponding to the highest frequency. To reduce this effective length, the solenoids are wound as close to the rod as possible and are usually provided with ferrite cheeks to confine the field to a minimum length. If the diameter of the rod inside the coil is large compared with the skin depth, eddy currents are induced and the output from the line is distorted. To avoid eddy currents and the frequency dispersion which occurs when the rod diameter is comparable with the wavelength, the delay medium must be in the form of very thin wire. For long delays, the length of wire required must be coiled in a spiral or helix if it is to occupy a reasonable space. Further dispersion is caused by this curvature of the wire and the effect of the wire supports; this can only be avoided when the compressional mode is used by making the radius of curvature large.

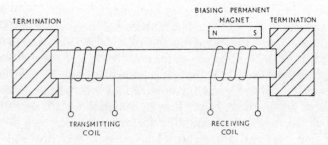

FIG. 2.8 *Magnetostrictive delay line*

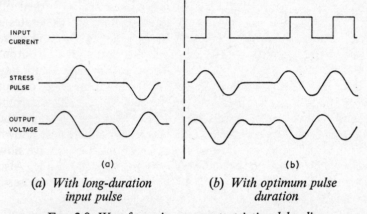

(a)   (b)

(*a*) *With long-duration*   (*b*) *With optimum pulse*
input pulse   *duration*

FIG. 2.9 *Waveforms in a magnetostrictive delay line*

With the torsional mode this curvature dispersion can be
eliminated by the use of a wire which has no inherent curvature
before coiling and there is no dispersion due to the finite diameter
of the wire. The velocity of propagation of torsional waves is
only 60 per cent of the velocity of the compressional mode so that
the delay per unit length is correspondingly increased. Figure 2.10
shows a method whereby torsional vibrations may be excited in a
wire which need not be magnetostrictive. Longitudinal vibrations
are excited in the tapes at equal distances from the wire, in which
they cause torsional vibrations to be set up.[17]

The ideal material for use in magnetostrictive delay lines should
have a low transmission loss, a negligible variation of delay with
temperature and a high electromechanical coupling factor. This
factor, which depends on the permeability and the magnetostriction coefficient, is a measure of the efficiency of the transducer

C

in converting magnetic energy to acoustic at the input, or acoustic to magnetic at the output. Nickel wire has been commonly used but suffers from the disadvantage of a fairly high temperature coefficient of delay time, some fourteen parts in 10^5 per °C which is slightly less than half that of a mercury line. This variation, however, is still too great for applications where long delays are required. Since there is no known material which combines a high electromechanical coupling factor with a low temperature coefficient, several expedients to overcome this problem have been employed. There is no reason, other than simplicity of

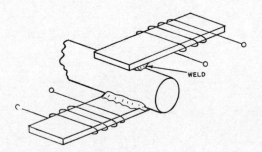

FIG. 2.10 *Excitation of torsional vibrations in a wire*

construction, why the transducer material should be the same as the transmission medium and units have been constructed in which two materials are welded together.[17] In other cases, the material enclosed by the transducer coils has been heat-treated separately to increase the efficiency of the transducer action without affecting the transmission properties of the remainder of the wire.[14]

Wire made of a nickel-iron-titanium alloy can be heat-treated to give a negligible temperature coefficient of delay, less than five parts in 10^6 per °C, and also introduces a low transmission loss.[17] Torsional magnetostrictive delay lines with a capacity of more than 6000 bits at a 2 Mc/s digit frequency have been constructed using this material.[16] Temperature compensation of magnetostrictive delay lines has been carried out by varying the position of one transducer coil along the wire. The coil is mounted on a pivoted lever which is moved by a bimetallic strip as the temperature changes.[12]

2.4 TEMPERATURE EFFECTS

Although the variation of delay with temperature can be made negligibly low in magnetostrictive delay lines, the variation in mercury delay lines is a significant factor limiting the maximum capacity of the unit. The temperature coefficient of delay is some three parts in 10^4 per °C, so that in a unit with a capacity of 1000 digits a change in temperature of 1°C will lead to a phase change in the output pulses of 0·3 of a digit period. Since the reliable operation of the system depends on the accurate positioning of

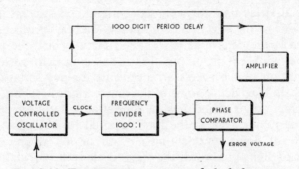

FIG. 2.11 *Temperature-compensated clock-frequency control system*

the clock-pulses with respect to the output from the line, some steps must be taken either to control the temperature accurately or to compensate for a change in temperature by altering the clock-pulse frequency. Figure 2.11 shows diagrammatically an arrangement whereby the clock frequency is controlled to compensate for temperature variations. The clock-pulse generator consists of a voltage-controlled oscillator. The clock frequency is divided in the same ratio as there are digit periods in the delay line, 1000 in the case illustrated. The output from the frequency divider is fed into the delay line and the phase of the output from the line compared with the output from the frequency divider. As the delay varies due to changes in temperature, an error voltage is generated which controls the frequency of the clock oscillator.

When several lines share a common clock-pulse generator, it is essential that all of them should be at the same temperature so that they have equal delay times. If all the delay lines are assembled

in a single unit of which the bulk is made of metal with a high thermal conductivity, it is fairly straightforward to maintain an even temperature and frequency compensation is easily applied. Due to the bulk and weight of the units, there is a limit to the number of lines which can be constructed in a single assembly. Since, in this case, steps must be taken to maintain all the separate units at the same temperature it is not difficult to extend the arrangement to control the temperature accurately.

2.5 ACCESS CIRCUITS

Since all delay-line stores are sequential-access systems in which time is one of the selection coordinates, the basic problem in this selection is the determination of the time at which the required word is available at the output of the delay unit. Before attempting a description of the access arrangements for any serial store, it will be helpful to define some of the time periods in such a system. The clock or digit period T is the time allocated to a single binary digit; the minor cycle is the time required for the passage of a sequence of digits representing a word or nT, where n is the number of digits in a word; the major cycle is the circulation time of a delay line in the main store or NnT, where N is the number of words stored in one delay line. When numbers are represented in binary form inside the system, it is convenient to make N equal to a power of 2, say 2^r so that the position of a word in the delay line is specified by r binary digits. The selection problem can now be defined as the determination within a major cycle, of the minor cycle corresponding to a given address of r binary digits.

The basis of the serial binary access system of Fig. 2.12(a) is the r-stage counter, counting minor cycles, which keeps track of the words as they circulate in the system. This counter constitutes an absolute time reference to the location of the stored information, which will, therefore, be inaccessible if the counter should miscount for any reason. When a particular word, whose address is contained in the address register, is to be located, the output from the counter is compared in the anti-coincidence unit with the number in the address register. The operation of the access circuits is illustrated in Fig. 2.12(b). As long as the number in the counter differs from that in the address register, the flip-flop f_1, which is set at the beginning of each minor cycle by the

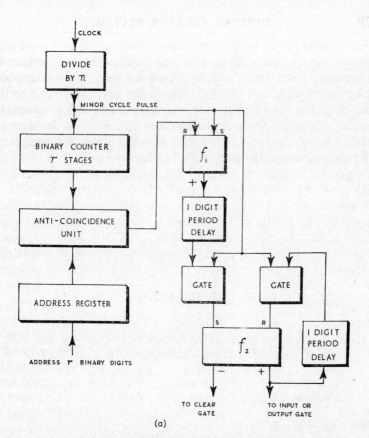

FIG. 2.12(a) *Block diagram of access arrangements for a delay-line store*

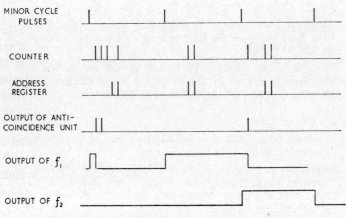

FIG. 2.12(b) *Waveforms in system of 2.12(a)*

minor-cycle pulse, is reset sometime during the cycle by the output of the anti-coincidence unit and the flip-flop f_2 is never set. However, when there is coincidence between the counter and address register, f_1 is not reset before the next minor-cycle pulse which passes through the gate and sets f_2. The following minor-cycle pulse resets f_2 whose output, therefore, is a waveform which lasts one minor cycle and whose position in the major cycle is determined uniquely by the address. If several delay lines are used to provide increased storage capacity, in addition to the time selection described above, spatial selection of the required line is necessary. This is carried out by a straightforward decoding operation in which other address digits route the output waveform from f_2 to the required delay line.

BIBLIOGRAPHY

GENERAL

1. Anderson, J. R. 'Electrical Delay Lines for Digital Computer Applications', *Trans. I.R.E. on Electronic Computers*, EC-2, pp. 5–13 (1953).

2. Scarrott, G. G., Harwood, W. J. and Johnson, K. C. 'Electromagnetic Delay Networks for Digital Storage', *Proc. I.E.E.* 103, Part B, Supplement No. 3, pp. 476–82 (1956).

MERCURY DELAY LINES

3. Sharpless, T. K. 'Design of Mercury Delay Lines', *Electronics*, 20 (ii), pp. 134–8 (November, 1947).

4. Wilkes, M. V. and Renwick, W. 'An Ultrasonic Memory Unit for the EDSAC', *Electronic Engineering*, 20, pp. 208–13 (July, 1948).

5. Auerbach, I. L., Eckert, J. P., Shaw, R. F. and Sheppard, C.B. 'Mercury Delay Line Using a Pulse Rate of Several Megacycles', *Proc. I.R.E.*, 40, pp. 828–35 (1952).

6. Newman, E. A., Clayden, D. O. and Wright, M. A. 'Mercury Delay Line Storage System of the ACE Pilot Model Electronic Computer', *Proc. I.E.E.*, 100, Part II, pp. 445–52 (1953).

QUARTZ DELAY LINES

7. Arenberg, D. L. 'Ultrasonic Solid Delay Lines', *Jour. Acoustical Society of America*, 20, pp. 1–26 (1948).

8. Spaeth, D. A., Rogers, T. F. and Johnson, S. J. 'Wide-Band Large Dynamic Range Fused-Quartz Delay Lines for Increased-Capacity High-Speed Computer Memories', *Convention Record of the I.R.E.*, 1954, Part 6, pp. 73–6.

9. Hammond, V. J. 'Quartz Delay Lines—The State of the Art', *British Communications and Electronics*, **9**, pp. 104–10 (1962).

MAGNETOSTRICTIVE DELAY LINES

10. Robbins, R. C. and Millership, R. 'Applications of Magnetostriction Delay Lines', *Proc. Symposium on Automatic Digital Computation*, held at the National Physical Laboratory, 1953., pp. 199–212, H.M.S.O. (London, 1954).

11. Scarrott, G. G. and Naylor, R. 'Wire-type Acoustic Delay Lines for Digital Storage', *Proc. I.E.E.*, **103**, Part B, Supplement No. 3, pp. 497–508 (1956).

12. Showell, H. A., Barrow, C. W. M. and Collis, R. E. 'Magnetostrictive Delay Line Store Operating at 1 Mc/s Using Transistor Circuits', *Proc. I.E.E.* **106**, Part B, Supplement No. 18, pp. 1267–76, 1289–91 (1959).

13. Williams, R. C. 'Theory of Magnetostrictive Delay Lines', *Trans. I.R.E. on Ultrasonics Engineering*, UE–7, pp. 16–38 (1959).

14. Aaronson, D. A. and James, D. B. 'Magnetostrictive Ultrasonic Delay Lines for a P.C.M. Communication System', *Trans. I.R.E. on Electronic Computers*, **EC–9**, pp. 329–32 (1960).

15. 'Bibliography on Magnetostrictive Delay Lines', *Trans. I.R.E. on Electronic Computers*, **EC–10**, p. 285 (1961).

16. Beck, R. M. 'PB-250—A High Speed Serial General-purpose Computer Using Magnetostrictive Delay Line Storage', *Proc. Eastern Joint Computer Conference*, December, 1960, pp. 283–97.

17. Rothbart, A. and Brown, A. J. 'What Designers Should Know About Magnetostrictive Delay Lines', *Electronics*, **35**, April 13th, 1962, pp. 55–9.

CHAPTER 3

ELECTROSTATIC AND
FERROELECTRIC STORAGE

THE storage of information making use of the ability of a dielectric to retain a pattern of electric charges has taken many
forms. In the early development of digital computers, charge-
storage systems played an important role and were incorporated
into several machines. The first random-access systems available
made use of electrostatic storage tubes, of which several types
were developed. Although no computing system now employs
this form of storage, for the sake of completeness and its historical
importance a brief description of the major developments in this
field will be given.

Although ferroelectric storage looks very attractive in principle,
the practical difficulties in producing a working store have not
yet been solved. The major advances in magnetic elements, which
have none of the drawbacks of the ferroelectric element, have
eliminated the need for further development in this area.

3.1 ELECTROSTATIC STORAGE TUBES

In all electrostatic storage tubes, the information is stored as a
pattern of electric charges on an isolated and electrically floating
surface. These charged spots, each corresponding to one binary
digit, are arranged in a two-dimensional array on the surface and
are located by the deflection of an electron beam along two coordinates. Since this deflection can be carried out rapidly, access
is essentially random, although it will obviously take longer to
move the beam from one corner of the array to the diagonally
opposite corner, than from one spot to an adjacent one.

An essential requirement for the operation of all electrostatic storage tubes is that the secondary emission ratio of the storage surface should be greater than unity for some range of primary electron velocity. The secondary emission ratio, which is defined as the average number of secondary electrons emitted by the

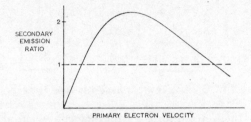

FIG. 3.1 *Secondary emission ratio against primary electron velocity*

surface for each primary incident electron, is shown as a function of primary electron velocity for a typical material in Fig. 3.1. It will be seen that, as the primary velocity, which depends on the potential between the cathode and final anode of the electron gun, is increased, the ratio is initially less than one but increases until more than one secondary electron is emitted for each primary. As the velocity increases further, the ratio again falls below unity.

3.1.1 WILLIAMS CATHODE-RAY-TUBE STORE

In the Williams tube,[1] named after its inventor Professor F. C. Williams, the charge patterns on small areas of the screen of a conventional cathode-ray tube are used to store binary information. These small areas, or spots, each of which represents one binary digit, are arranged in a two-dimensional array and are selected by means of the normal X and Y deflection plates. To detect the rate of change of charge on the surface during reading, a signal plate is placed close to the screen of the cathode-ray tube (C.R.T.), as shown in Fig. 3.2. When the electron beam impinges on a spot on the screen, more electrons are emitted from the spot than are incident on it, if the secondary emission ratio is more than one. The net loss of electrons from the spot causes its potential to become positive with respect to the conductive coating in the C.R.T. which collects the excess electrons. This rise in potential will continue until its retarding effect on the electrons leaving the

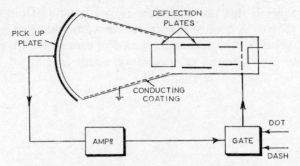

FIG. 3.2 *Parts of cathode-ray-tube store*

spot causes them to return to the screen, when the effective secondary emission ratio drops to unity. Some of the secondary electrons return to the area of the screen around the spot, causing a potential distribution as shown in Fig. 3.3(*a*). If the beam is now turned off and moved to a spot immediately adjacent to the first one and then turned on again, the potential distribution of Fig. 3.3(*a*) is also established at the second spot. When the separation of the spots is less than a certain critical distance, some of the secondary electrons emitted from the second spot are attracted by the positive potential of the first. The potential at the first spot is therefore reduced, resulting in the distribution shown in Fig. 3.3(*b*). The potential distributions of Fig. 3.3 can be used to represent the digits 0 and 1, the single spot or 'dot' representing 0 and the double spot, which can be drawn out into a 'dash', representing 1.

When the electron beam is again switched on to a spot with the potential distribution of Fig. 3.3(*a*), only a small change in surface charge is required to make good that lost by leakage, causing a negligible output current from the pickup plate. However, when the beam is switched on, a cloud of electrons is introduced near the pickup plate, causing a transient current to flow, and a similar current of opposite polarity flows when the beam is turned off. The resulting output from the amplifier is shown in Fig. 3.4(*a*). When the electron beam is switched on to the first spot of the double spot distribution of Fig. 3.3(*b*), the current flowing into the pickup plate is the sum of three effects. Firstly, there is the transient current due to the electron cloud; secondly, there is the contribution due to restoring the positive potential at the first spot; thirdly, a current flows due to the secondary electrons levelling the potential at the second spot. Fortunately, the second effect takes place much more rapidly than the third, so that the output from the amplifier is as shown in Fig. 3.4(*b*). Comparing this with the output from the amplifier in Fig. 3.4(*a*), it will be seen that both the polarity and the amplitude are different.

Since the charge distribution on the surface of the screen does decay due to leakage effects, the stored information must be regenerated periodically, if indefinite storage time is required. Reading automatically regenerates a dot but, in the case of a dash, the beam must be turned on to the adjacent spot to rewrite the dash. In the first application of the Williams tube, one information word was read serially, by scanning one line on the screen. Interlaced with the access to selected words, the lines were periodically scanned to regenerate the information. The deflection voltage, applied to the X plates, scans repetitively the digits in the word or line, the Y deflection voltage is changed to that corresponding to

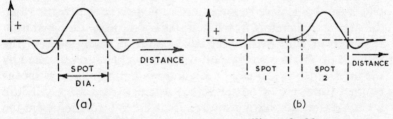

(*a*) *at single spot*   (*b*) *at double spot*

FIG. 3.3 *Potential distribution on screen*

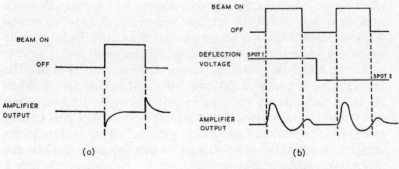

(*a*) *a single spot*   (*b*) *a double spot*

FIG. 3.4 *Waveforms due to bombarding*

the next required line. The digits of a word may also be read or written in parallel, by storing each digit of a word in corresponding spots on different C.R.T.s, all of which have the same voltages applied to their deflection plates.[2] In this case, access to the required word is obtained by converting the address digits to two analogue voltages which are applied respectively to the X and Y deflection plates. The operation of the parallel system again takes place in two alternate cycles, an action cycle in which access is gained to the required word, followed by a regeneration cycle in which the words are rewritten periodically to maintain the stored pattern.

Several variations on the double spot or 'dot-dash' mode of operation of a C.R.T. store have been described. The charge distribution on the surface can be altered by defocussing the beam, without altering its position, giving the 'focus-defocus' mode. Alternatively, the beam can be made to trace a small circle round the dot giving the 'circle-dot' representation. The packing density which can be achieved on the surface is determined by the beam diameter and therefore by the sharpness of the focus obtained from the electron gun. Because of deflection-defocussing effects, it is difficult to obtain a small spot over the complete screen area and the area which is available for storage is limited. Since electrons emitted from a spot on the screen which is read repeatedly are attracted to neighbouring storage areas, the information stored in adjacent spots will eventually be destroyed. The number of times a spot can be read before destroying the information stored in neighbouring spots is usually named the 'read-around ratio'. If no restrictions are placed on the number of successive times one word can be selected, the read-around ratio must be greater than the number of bits stored on one tube, since this determines the regeneration period. Stores with capacities up to 1024 digits per tube have been successfully operated with parallel read-out.

An incidental advantage of the regeneration process is that the system is proof against long-term drifts in the deflection voltages. As these vary, the stored pattern drifts over the surface of the screen but the information remains intact, since it is periodically rewritten. The only requirement is that the variation during one complete regeneration period must be small enough to allow the information to be read correctly.

3.1.2 BARRIER-GRID STORAGE TUBE

Binary information can be stored on an insulating surface by storing charges at two different potential levels. These levels can be set up on the surface by applying a voltage pulse to the pickup plate, which is capacitively coupled to the surface during writing. The essential parts of a barrier-grid tube are shown in Fig. 3.5. In addition to the conventional electron gun and deflection system, the tube contains the dielectric storage surface, usually mica, on the back of which the back electrode, or pickup plate, is deposited. Mounted close to the front of the surface is the collector grid which collects all the secondary electrons emitted. The barrier grid itself is mounted very close to the dielectric. Since the collector potential is

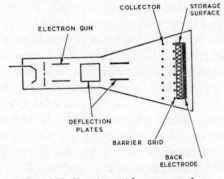

FIG. 3.5 *Barrier-grid storage tube*

usually positive by some 200 to 300 volts with respect to the barrier grid, efficient collection of secondary electrons is ensured by the resultant uniform electric field. Both the collector and grid are made of a mesh of orthogonal wires which are made very fine, so that few electrons in the beam are intercepted. By arranging that the wires in the two meshes make an angle of 45° with each other, the masking effect of the collector on the barrier-grid openings is minimized.

When a small area of the storage surface is illuminated by the electron beam, there is a net flow of electrons from the surface, since the secondary emission ratio is greater than unity. The spot, therefore, becomes positively charged, causing some electrons to return to it. An equilibrium potential, slightly positive with respect to the potential of the barrier grid, which may be taken as earth, is eventually reached when the number of electrons leaving is exactly balanced by the number arriving. When the beam is turned off, the spot will remain at the equilibrium potential. Suppose now that a negative pulse of 100 volts, say, is applied to the back electrode before the beam is turned on. This capacitively lowers the potential level of the whole of the storage surface by nearly 100 volts. If the electron beam is now turned on, the spot will again charge to the same equilibrium potential slightly more positive than the barrier grid. When the beam is turned off and the voltage of the back electrode returns to normal, the potential of the storage surface increases by 100 volts, leaving the spot positive with respect to the barrier grid by some 100 volts. This potential level may be taken to represent a stored 1, while the normal equilibrium potential of approximately 0 volts may be taken to represent 0.

To read the stored information, the beam is turned on to a spot and the current flowing in the back electrode circuit amplified and detected. If the spot was previously charged positively, the beam current rapidly discharges it to the normal equilibrium potential, causing a negative current to flow in the sensing circuit. If the spot was initially in the state corresponding to a stored 0, no output current flows. As in the case of the Williams tube, reading destroys the stored information and it is therefore necessary to rewrite it, if indefinite storage time is required. Since the system is also subject to leakage and interaction between adjacent spots, the information must be regenerated periodically.

The barrier-grid tube has the advantage over the cathode-ray tube that the packing density can be much higher, since secondary electrons emitted by the storage surface are removed by the collector. Since no secondary electrons return to neighbouring areas, there is less interaction between adjacent spots. Packing densities as high as 128×128 on one storage surface with an access-cycle time of 2·5 microseconds have been achieved.[7]

3.1.3 HOLDING-GUN TUBE

Both the barrier-grid tube and the Williams tube suffer from the disadvantage that information must be regenerated frequently because of leakage from the storage surface. The use of a second electron gun, the holding gun, eliminates this dynamic regeneration and substitutes static holding, in which the charge lost by leakage is replaced by a flood of low-velocity electrons. The reading and writing operations are very similar to those in the barrier-grid tube, while the holding gun makes use of the secondary emission characteristic of the storage surface to maintain the stored charges at their equilibrium potentials. Figure 3.6 shows the arrangement inside a holding-gun tube. The read-write gun is a conventional high-velocity system with electrostatic deflection for selection. The

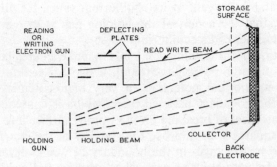

FIG. 3.6 *Holding-gun tube*

holding gun provides a spray of low-velocity electrons flooding the
surface, which consists of a mosaic of beryllium squares, with a
high secondary emission ratio, on a mica dielectric. Mounted close
to the front of the storage surface is a collecting grid which collects
secondary electrons. Behind the dielectric is the back electrode or
pickup plate. In the tube, the digit 1, say, is represented by a charge
stored at the level of the collector potential, 0 volts, and the digit 0
at the level of the holding-gun cathode—100 volts. These charges
are written in exactly the same way as they are in the barrier-grid
tube and may be read in a similar manner.

When the electrons from the holding gun approach an area on
the surface which is near the cathode potential of the holding gun,
they either strike the surface with a very low energy or return to
the collector. If the potential of the spot is more negative than the
equilibrium value, all the electrons return to the collector and the
spot charges positively, due to leakage. On the other hand, if the
potential of the spot is more positive than normal, some electrons
do reach the surface but with a velocity at which the secondary
emission ratio is less than unity. The accumulation of electrons
charges the spot negatively, so that only enough electrons reach
the surface to maintain the spots at the potential of the holding-gun
cathode. Electrons reaching areas of the surface at collector
potential arrive with a velocity corresponding to 100 volts approximately, when the secondary emission ratio of the surface is greater
than unity. When the surface is slightly below the equilibrium
potential, the net loss of electrons charges it positively until it
reaches equilibrium. If, on the other hand, the surface is above
collector potential, electrons are attracted back to the spot until

the potential falls again to its equilibrium value. It will be seen, therefore, that the action of the holding gun is to maintain the surface at either of its equilibrium values.

The action of the holding gun tends to make an area held at one of the equilibrium potentials expand. If two adjacent areas are at different equilibrium potentials, a very high potential gradient exists at the boundary between them, which is consequently unstable. The effect of breaking up the storage surface into a mosaic of small squares is to improve the stability of the stored pattern and to prevent changes in the boundary between adjacent spots. The high-velocity electron gun, when reading and writing, overrides the effect of the holding gun, which is always turned on. One disadvantage of this form of static regeneration is the high degree of stability required in the deflection circuits, which must always locate the same area of the screen for the same address.

3.1.4 THE SELECTRON

The principle of operation of the selectron, or selective electrostatic storage tube, is similar to the operation of the holding-gun tube, although its structure is considerably different. The major difference is in the way a storage cell is selected. Instead of deflecting the electron beam by a conventional deflection system, selection voltages are applied to groups of perpendicular selecting bars, which only allow electrons to pass through the selected window to the storage cell. The storage cells consist of metal buttons with a hole through their centres, each separately made and completely

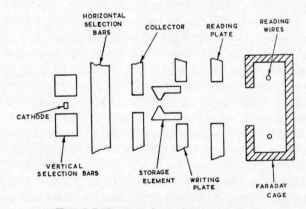

FIG. 3.7 *Section through the Selectron*

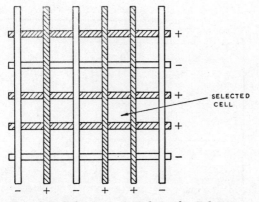

FIG. 3.8 *Selection principle in the Selectron*

isolated from the rest of the electrode structure when assembled. A much-simplified section through one element in the selectron is shown in Fig. 3.7. Writing into a cell is accomplished by selecting the required cell and storing a charge on it at either cathode potential, 0 volts, or collector potential, +200 volts. The potential at which the charge is stored is controlled by a voltage pulse applied to the writing plate, which operates in the same way as the back electrode in the barrier-grid or holding-gun tube.

The state of a cell is sensed by detecting the current flow through the central hole in the storage element. When the element is at its negative equilibrium potential, electrons are repelled from the element and no current flows. When the element is positive the electrons passing through the hole are detected by reading wires. These are electrostatically screened by a Faraday cage to eliminate pickup from the large amplitude pulses applied to the other electrodes. While the tube is not actively being used for reading or writing, electrons are allowed to pass to every cell and maintain the stored charges at their equilibrium potentials. The reading plate acts as a grid to cut off current to the reading wires, except when the reading operation is taking place.

The selection principle is illustrated in Fig. 3.8. As long as the bar on one side of a window is biased negatively, electrons cannot pass from the cathode to the collector. Although three horizontal and three vertical bars in Fig. 3.9 have been biased positively, only one window has all sides positive and is therefore selected. Because a window is only selected when positive potentials are applied to two adjacent horizontal and two adjacent vertical bars, combinatorial

D

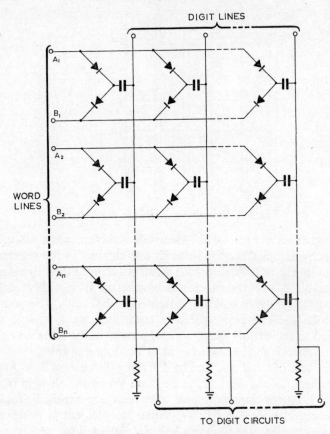

DIGIT LINES

WORD LINES

TO DIGIT CIRCUITS

FIG. 3.9 *Diode-capacitor storage system*

methods of connecting the bars in groups can be used, resulting in a very considerable reduction in the number of selection
leads required. For example, in the tube with 256 cells which
was successfully developed,[10] only eighteen external connections
to the selection bars are required.

3.2 DIODE-CAPACITOR STORAGE

Another form of charge storage, which has been used in several
digital computers, makes use of discrete capacitor elements which
are selected by means of rectifier diodes. The capacitors can be
charged to two different potentials representing the two binary
digits. For example, we may take a voltage, $+V$ volts, to represent

1 and $-V$ volts to represent 0. The operation of the system shown in Fig. 3.9 is more easily understood by referring the waveforms shown in Fig. 3.10. Except when reading or writing is taking place, the word lines A and B are held at $-V$ and $+V$ respectively, so that the selection diodes are then reverse biased and, therefore, of high resistance. To read the state of the capacitors common to one word, both A and B are brought to earth potential, causing the capacitors to discharge through the digit line terminating resistors. If a capacitor was initially charged to $+V$, a negative current will flow, giving a negative voltage output across its resistor, as shown

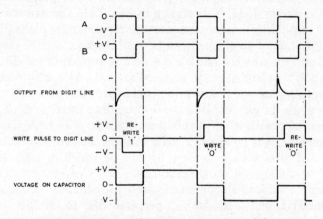

FIG. 3.10 *Waveforms illustrating operation of the system in Fig. 3.9*

in Fig. 3.10. Since the charge on a capacitor is destroyed by reading, the information must be rewritten. A 1 is rewritten by applying a negative pulse, $-V$ volts in amplitude, to the digit line. The capacitor is recharged and left charged to $+V$ at the end of the cycle. To write 0 into the element, a positive pulse of $+V$ volts is applied to the digit line and the capacitor is charged to a negative potential.

The diode-capacitor store suffers from the usual disadvantage of all charge storage systems, the decay of the stored charge due to leakage resulting in the need for periodic regeneration. The time constant with which the charge decays exponentially depends mainly on the reverse resistance of the selection diodes, since this is usually much less than the leakage resistance of the capacitor itself. Although the cost per bit of a diode-capacitor store is relatively large compared with other systems, it does offer the advantages which result from operating with relatively large pulse amplitudes.

3.3   FERROELECTRIC STORAGE

In certain dielectric materials, states of permanent polarization can exist, which are analogous to ferromagnetic remanent induction. Some of these ferroelectric materials exhibit a rectangular hysteresis-loop characteristic, when polarization, P, is plotted against applied electric field, E, as shown in Fig. 3.11. The two remanent states of polarization may be taken to represent the digits 0 and 1 and the state of an element can be read by detecting the displacement current which flows when a field is applied in the direction shown. If the element was initially in the 1 state, a large displacement current flows as the polarization is changed. Only a small current flows when the element is in the 0 state, since there is only a small change of polarization in this case. Because the characteristic is rectangular, it is possible to write into the element by the coincidence of two voltage pulses, neither of which is sufficient by itself to change the polarization. An array of elements can be fabricated by depositing a set of parallel conductors on one side of the material and a similar set, perpendicular to the first, on the other side. Such an array is shown in Fig. 3.12 with word conductors deposited on one side and digit conductors on the other. One word is read out in parallel, by applying a positive voltage pulse to the selected word line and detecting the amplitude of the current flowing in the terminating resistors. To write into a word, a negative voltage pulse is applied to the selected word line and a positive pulse to those digit lines into which 1 has to be written.

Although the ferroelectric store has the apparent advantages of simplicity of manufacture and a high packing density, there are some practical difficulties which have never been successfully overcome. Unlike a ferromagnetic material, which has an absolute coercive force, the coercive force of a ferroelectric decreases with the frequency of the applied electric field. The element will, therefore, switch with a low field if applied for a long enough time or, since the effect is cumulative, if a sufficient number of voltage pulses is applied. Digit-write pulses, therefore, tend to destroy the information in unselected elements, so that the information in the

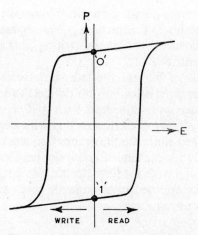

FIG. 3.11 *Polarization as a function of electric field for a ferroelectric*

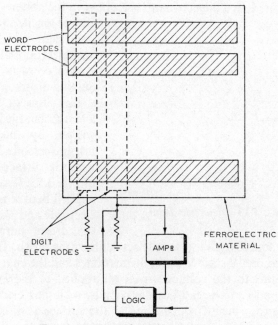

FIG. 3.12 *Ferroelectric storage system*

store must be regenerated periodically. As the writing time is increased, the number of disturbing pulses necessary to destroy the information increases, so that the writing time must be long for satisfactory operation.

Single crystals of barium titanate show suitable polarization-applied field characteristics but are difficult to grow with a large enough area to accommodate more than 1000 cells. In addition, the temperature sensitivity of the material and the heat dissipation in a cell when switched limit the maximum frequency at which the cell can be switched to some tens of kilocycles per second. There is less flexibility in design with the ferroelectric element, since it has only two terminals as opposed to a magnetic core, which may have as many windings as required.

3.4   DIELECTRIC DRUM

In this system, which is analogous to the magnetic drum, information is stored on a dielectric surface, either in the pattern of surface charge or in the form of polarized regions in a ferroelectric material. The system consists of a conducting drum, coated with a thin film of dielectric, and the charge pattern is written by means of a brush electrode in contact with the surface as shown in Fig. 3.13. If a voltage is applied between the brush electrode and the metal of the drum, current flows from the source to charge the dielectric under the brush. This charge is retained on the surface as the drum rotates and the charge pattern corresponds to the voltage waveform applied to the brush. The information can be read destructively by a similar electrode and detecting the current which flows as the surface is discharged. If the electrode is not in contact with the surface but only coupled capacitively, the charge pattern induces an output signal as the drum rotates and the information can be read non-destructively.

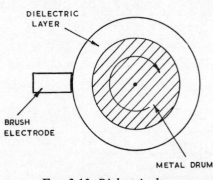

DIELECTRIC LAYER

BRUSH ELECTRODE

METAL DRUM

FIG. 3.13 *Dielectric drum*

Since the surface charge decays due to leakage effects, the system must be operated regeneratively if an indefinite storage time is required. Alternatively, if a ferroelectric material were used, the system would be the electric analogue of the magnetic drum and information would be stored indefinitely. However, in comparison with the magnetic drum (see Chapter 4), the dielectric drum offers no advantages and, since no suitable ferroelectric material has been developed, has the severe disadvantage of requiring regeneration of the stored information.

3.5 STORAGE BY CHARGE PENETRATION INTO PLASTIC TAPE

A recently described electrostatic recording system[19,20] uses charge penetration into certain plastic insulating materials, giving a permanent record which can be read repeatedly and stored almost indefinitely. The charge is injected into the material by passing it under a knife-edge electrode, between which and a back electrode a potential is applied as shown in Fig. 3.14. The information stored is read by passing the tape through a similar system of electrodes between which a potential is induced by the charge in the tape. Unwanted signals, during reading, are caused by the surface charge on the tape due to the recording process and friction in the tape transport mechanism. The signal-to-noise ratio is

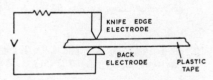

FIG. 3.14 *Electrode assembly for injecting charge into plastic tape*

improved when these surface charges are first removed by passing the tape through an ion cloud produced by a high-voltage corona discharge.

This system has never been used for the storage of digital information for which magnetic-tape systems (see Chapter 4) offer considerable advantages.

BIBLIOGRAPHY

C.R.T. STORE
 1. Williams, F. C. and Kilburn, T. 'A Storage System for Use with Binary Digital Computing Machines', *Proc. I.E.E.*, **96**, Part III, pp. 81–100 (1949).

2. Edwards, D. B. G. 'The Design and Operation of a Parallel-type Cathode-Ray-Tube Storage System', *Proc. I.E.E.*, **103**, Part B, Supplement No. 2 (Convention on Digital Computer Techniques), pp. 319–26 (1956).

3. Wong, S. Y. 'High-Density Williams Storage', *I.R.E. Trans. Electronic Computers*, EC–4, pp. 351–6 (1956).

4. Williams, F. C., Kilburn, T., Litting, C. N. W., Edwards, D. G. B. and Hoffman, G. R. 'Recent Advances in Cathode Ray Storage', *Proc. I.E.E.*, Part II, **100**, pp. 523–43 (1953).

BARRIER-GRID TUBE

5. Jensen, A. S., Smith, J. P., Mesner, M. H. and Flory, L. E. 'The Barrier Grid Storage Tube and Its Operation', *R.C.A. Review*, **9**, pp. 112–33 (1948).

6. Hines, M. E., Chruney, M. and McCarthy, J. A. 'Digital Memory in Barrier-Grid Storage Tubes', *Bell System Tech. Jour.*, **34**, pp. 1241–64 (1955).

7. Greenwood, T. S., and Staehler, R. E. 'A High-speed Barrier-grid Store', *Bell System Tech. Jour.*, **37**, pp. 1195–220 (1958).

HOLDING-GUN TUBE

8. Haeff, A. V. 'A Memory Tube', *Electronics*, **20**, pp. 80–93 (September, 1947).

9. Dodd, S. H., Klemperer, H. and Youtz, P. 'Electrostatic Storage Tube', *Electrical Engineering*, **69**, pp. 990–5 (1950).

SELECTRON

10. Rajchman, J. A. 'The Selective Electrostatic Storage Tube', *R.C.A. Review*, **12**, pp. 53–97 (1951).

DIODE-CAPACITOR STORAGE

11. Holt, A. W. 'An Experimental Rapid Access Memory Using Diodes and Capacitors', *Proc. of the Association for Computing Machinery Meeting* at Toronto, Ontario, September, 1952, pp. 133–41.

12. Kaufman, M. M. 'Millimicrosecond Diode-Capacitor Memory', *Proc. National Electronics Conference*, pp. 215–25 (October, 1959).

13. Conway, A. C. 'A Fast Random-Access Diode-Capacitor Store Using Transistors', *Proc. I.E.E.*, **106**, Part B, Supplement No. 16, pp. 659–62 (1959).

FERROELECTRIC STORAGE

14. Anderson, J. R. 'Ferroelectric Elements for Digital Computers and Switching Systems', *Electrical Engineering*, **71**, pp. 916–22 (1952).

15. Pulvari, C. F. 'Memory Matrix Using Ferroelectric Condensers as Bistable Elements', *Jour. Association for Computing Machinery*, **2**, pp. 169–85 (1955).

16. Campbell, D. S. 'Barium Titanate and Its Use as a Memory Store', *Jour. Brit. I.R.E.*, **17**, pp. 385–95 (1957).

17. Prutton, M. 'Ferroelectrics and Computer Storage', *Jour. Brit. I.R.E.*, **19**, pp. 93–9 (1959).

DIELECTRIC DRUM

18. Morleigh, S. 'A Dielectric Drum Storage System', *Jour. Brit. I.R.E.*, **21**, pp. 211–19 (1961).

CHARGE PENETRATION

19. Richardson, D. E. 'Improvements in or Relating to a Transducer System or Method', *Brit. Pat.*, Specifications Nos. 896,691 and 896,692 (May, 1962).

20. Richardson, D. E., Brophy, J. J., Seiwatz, H., Dickens, J. E. and Kerr, R. J. 'A System of Electrostatic Recording', *Trans. I.R.E. on Audio*, **AU–10**, pp. 95–8 (1962).

CHAPTER 4

MAGNETIC-SURFACE RECORDING

IN MAGNETIC-SURFACE recording, information is stored by magnetizing separate elements on a continuous magnetic medium to one of a set of distinct patterns of remanent magnetization. For example, in a binary recording, each element corresponds to one bit, and two patterns of magnetization, representing the digits 0 and 1, can be recorded. The information is read by passing the medium close to a reading head in which an e.m.f. is induced by the change of flux caused by the pattern of magnetization on the tape. Similarly, the information can be written by subjecting the medium to the magnetic field from a writing head, in which the recording current is flowing. Figure 4.1 shows a typical arrangement, in which the field in the gap of the record head impresses a change of magnetization in the magnetic medium in the close vicinity of the gap. As a change of magnetization passes under the gap in the read-head, an e.m.f. is induced in the coil. Digital recording differs from analogue recording, since it requires only two levels of magnetization. These are made as different from each other as possible, by employing saturation recording in which the medium is always left in one or other of its two remanent states. As well as improving the signal-to-noise ratio, saturation recording eliminates the need for a separate erasing operation, since new information can be written over any previously recorded pattern.

4.1 METHODS OF RECORDING

In Fig. 4.2 three methods of saturation recording are illustrated. Figure 4.2(*a*) shows pulse or return-to-saturation (RS) recording, in which the magnetic medium is magnetized to one state of remanence, except in elements where a 1 is stored, when the

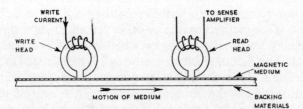

FIG. 4.1 *Magnetic surface recording arrangement*

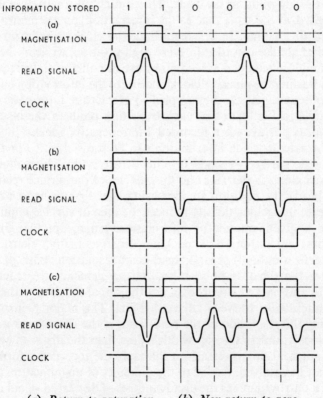

(a) *Return to saturation*   (b) *Non-return-to-zero*
(c) *Phase-modulation*

FIG. 4.2 *Methods of saturation recording*

magnetization is reversed for part of the element length. In Fig. 4.2(b) non-return-to-zero (NRZ) recording is illustrated. Here the medium is magnetized to one or other remanent state throughout the element length, depending on whether 1 or 0 is stored. In Fig. 4.2(c) the first half of an element storing 1 is magnetized to negative remanence and the second half to positive remanence, while, in an element storing 0, the states are reversed. This form of recording is equivalent to a phase reversal of the pattern and is usually known as phase-modulation (PM) recording. To recover the recorded information, some form of timing waveform is essential, both to indicate the digit period and to strobe the output signal at an appropriate point in the cycle. This timing information is usually recorded, at the same time as the information, on a separate 'clock track' or channel. In RS recording, the clock usually takes the form of a pulse recorded in every digit position, while in the NRZ method it is recorded as a square wave at half the digit frequency. By adjusting the phase of clock relative to the information channel, the output signal can be sampled to extract the information. For example in Fig. 4.2(c), at each transition point of the clock, the output is positive for a recorded 1 and negative for 0.

The rate at which information can be transferred to or from a magnetic surface depends on the density with which digits are packed along the surface and the velocity of the surface relative to the heads. In addition to increasing the digit transfer rate, an increase in packing density reduces the area of surface required to store a given amount of information. There are two primary factors which limit the packing density; firstly, element de-magnetization and, second, read-head resolution, both of which reduce the signal-to-noise ratio. As the elements are reduced in length and packed closer together, the signal output is reduced by the interaction between adjacent digits. The major factor determining the resolution of the read-head, is the effective gap-width. Obviously, unless the gap-width is less than the distance between two adjacent flux reversals on the tape, the recorded information cannot be resolved. Added to the difficulty of manufacture, a head with a narrow gap has the disadvantages of decreased signal output and increased sensitivity to variations in head-to-surface spacing.

Because only one flux reversal is required per digit element with NRZ recording, while two are required with the other methods described above, NRZ recording gives twice the digit transfer rate for the same density of flux reversals on the surface. However,

NRZ requires a response from the amplifiers extending from zero frequency up to half the digit frequency, while the range for PM recording is from half the digit frequency up to the digit frequency. The need for a d.c. response can have a significant effect on the cost of heads and amplifiers, especially when the packing density is high. Other factors, which may determine the performance of a magnetic head, are its self-inductance and self-resonant frequency.

The usual magnetic read-head gives an output which is proportional to the rate of change of flux, and is, therefore, unsuitable for sensing a stationary or slow-moving surface. Where static-reading is a requirement, either a variable reluctance or Hall effect head can be used. As its name implies, a variable reluctance head detects stationary magnetic fields by periodically changing the reluctance of the magnetic path and hence the flux linkage in the output circuit. The variation of reluctance may be induced mechanically by changing the length of a secondary air gap in the magnetic circuit. If the variation is induced electrically, by making use of the non-linear characteristic of the magnetic material, the response of the head may be extended to much higher frequencies (or tape speeds).[6] Here, the permeability of part of the magnetic circuit is varied by the application of a high-frequency m.m.f. and the output signal then consists of this carrier frequency amplitude-modulated by the flux linkage from the tape. The Hall effect is produced by the interaction of a magnetic field and current flow in a conducting or semiconducting material. When a conducting bar, in which a current is flowing, is subjected to a magnetic field at right angles to the direction of current flow, an electric field is produced, perpendicular both to the applied field and to the current. The Hall effect is much more pronounced in semiconducting materials, in which it can be used to sense either stationary or moving magnetic fields.

4.2 MAGNETIC DRUMS

In the magnetic drum the magnetic medium is deposited on the surface of a circular cylinder, as shown in Fig. 4.3. Both sprayed oxide and electro-deposited nickel, nickel-iron or nickel-cobalt surfaces have been used. The information, which is stored on parallel tracks around the drum, is written and read by magnetic heads as the drum revolves on its axis. Each track may have its own head, or a head-positioning mechanism[10] may be used to locate a common head to the required track as shown in Fig. 4.4. The magnetic drum suffers from the disadvantage of sequential access since, on average, it is necessary to wait for half of one revolution of the drum to locate the required information. An additional delay occurs when the information required is on a different track from that at present selected. The delay is due to the time taken, either to select the head corresponding to the wanted track, or for the head-positioning mechanism to move to the selected track. Switching to the selected head can be carried out by electromechanical relays or, if higher speed is required, by electronic switches.

The digits in a data-word are usually recorded serially along a track, so that each track is divided into sectors corresponding to one storage location. The digits of a word can also be recorded simultaneously in separate tracks, if parallel operation is required. To obviate the problem of accurate head-location introduced by the use of separate read- and write-heads, it is usual to employ the same head for reading and writing. Synchronization is achieved by deriving all timing waveforms from a pre-recorded clock track on the drum itself. In some applications where the drum is the only synchronous unit in the system, the system clock is also derived from the clock track on the drum. In other applications, where the system clock must be synchronous with some other unit (an ultra-sonic delay-line store, for example), the angular velocity of the drum must be controlled to maintain the two clocks in synchronism.[11] Figure 4.5 shows diagrammatically one method of synchronizing a drum. The output of the clock track is compared with the system clock in the phase comparator circuit, the output from which controls the current in the braking coils. If the drum tends to rotate too fast, the phase of the drum clock will be advanced on the system clock, thus causing an increase of current in the braking coils which reduces the drum speed. Similarly, if the drum tends to rotate too slowly, the current in the braking coils is reduced.

The radius of the drum is determined by the digit-packing density around the drum and the capacity of one track, while the required access time determines the angular velocity of the drum. In applications where the digit-transfer rate from the drum is fixed by the necessity for synchronous operation, the access time is directly proportional to the number of digits stored on one track. The choice of the drum parameters must, therefore, be a compromise between reducing access time and increasing capacity.

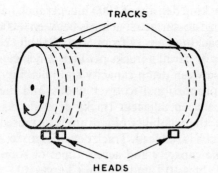

FIG. 4.3 *Magnetic drum with individual heads for each track*

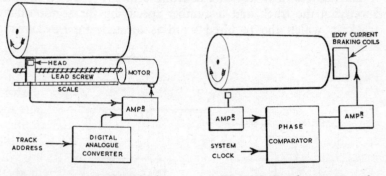

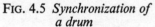

FIG. 4.4 *Magnetic drum with head-locating mechanism*

FIG. 4.5 *Synchronization of a drum*

When capacity must be maximized, the access time must be increased to reduce the mechanical stress at the surface of the drum to a safe value. Since this stress is proportional to the product of the radius and the square of the angular velocity, it is therefore proportional to the ratio of track capacity to packing density and inversely proportional to the square of the access time. The packing density depends on the effective gap-width of the head and one of the factors determining this is the head-to-surface spacing. This is influenced by the degree of uniformity of the surface finish, the eccentricity of the drum on its axis, the effect of wear on the bearings and differential thermal expansion between the drum and the head mounting. In some high-density drum applications, the head is run virtually in contact with the drum, being separated only by a thin film of oil.[15] With the spacing of 0·0002 in. so achieved, a packing density of 1000 bits per inch has been realized. Usually the head-to-surface spacing is between 0·0005 in. and 0·001 in., giving a packing density from 50 to 200 bits per inch.

The number of parallel tracks per inch which can be utilized is a compromise between drum capacity and reliability. Since the output signal is proportional to track width, and the 'cross-talk' or interference between adjacent tracks depends on the separation between them, the reliability of a drum is increased as the number of tracks per inch is reduced. Track densities up to 30 per inch have been used. The capacity and access times of some typical drums are given in Tables 10.1 and 10.2 in Chapter 10.

4.2.1   DRUM-ACCESS CIRCUITS

The address of a word on a drum is in two parts, a number specifying the track and a number specifying the sector of the track in which the required word is located. Figure 4.6 is a

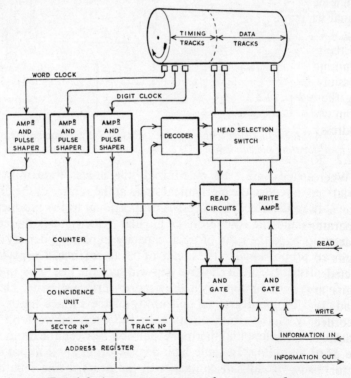

FIG. 4.6 *Access arrangements for magnetic drum*

schematic diagram of the access circuits of a typical magnetic-drum storage system. A drum is a sequential-access system in which time acts as one of the selection coordinates. It is, therefore, necessary to keep an accurate count of words as they pass the read/write station so that any word can be located. Each sector, which corresponds to one storage location on a track, is marked by a pulse recorded on a separate word-clock track. These pulses are fed to a counter which is reset to zero by a pulse occurring once every revolution of the drum, so that the sector passing the head at any time is uniquely determined by the number in the counter. When coincidence occurs between the number in the counter and the address digits specifying the sector, either the read gate is opened, allowing the required word of information to pass from the store, or the write gate allows new information to be written in the location. The remaining digits in the address specify the track and, when decoded, they control the head-selection switch. When a single head is used, the track digits are converted to an analogue signal which controls the track-locating mechanism, as shown in Fig. 4.4. Variations on the above system are possible. For example, all the timing information can be derived from the digit clock by counting down to the word-clock rate. Another variation, which is possibly less susceptible to error, eliminates the counter by recording the address of each sector on an address track, the output from which is compared with the address of the required sector.

4.2.2 REGENERATIVE TRACKS

Where the properties of a serial regenerative type store, like a delay line, are required, separate read- and write-heads, spaced apart by the number of digits to be stored, can be connected as shown in Fig. 4.7. As digits are read by the leading head, they are immediately re-recorded by the write-head. After a delay equal to the time it takes the drum to rotate through the sector between the heads, the recorded digits are again read.

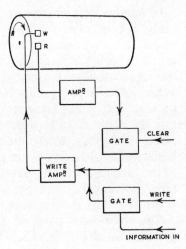

FIG. 4.7 *Regenerative track operation of a magnetic drum*

E

This system is used in an identical way to the delay-line store described in Chapter 2.

4.3   MAGNETIC TAPE

The use of magnetic tape for digital storage was a development from the tape equipment for sound recording and reproduction. As the name implies, the magnetic surface in this case is deposited on a long flexible strip, which is usually wound on reels. Information is stored in tracks, the number depending on the tape width, and is read or written as the tape passes a head assembly, while unwinding from one reel on to another. Because the information is stored sequentially along the tape, the maximum access time is the time taken to wind the tape completely from one reel to another and is in the order of minutes. On the other hand, the storage capacity of one reel of tape, 3600 ft long and 1 in. wide, for example, is more than 100 million binary digits. Since tape units are usually arranged to make reels easily changeable, the storage capacity is virtually unlimited. Although metal tapes and wires have been employed, the most common tape is a plastic backing tape with a layer of iron oxide deposited on the surface.

4.3.1 TAPE TRANSPORT MECHANISMS

In applications where a reel of tape can be scanned continuously, a conventional tape mechanism, similar to those used in sound recording, can be used. These have facilities for running the tape through at a constant speed in one direction and rewinding the tape, usually at a higher speed, in the opposite direction. When intermittent operation is required, the unit must be able to stop and start the tape moving in either direction and as quickly as possible. To ensure that the start and stop times are not limited by the acceleration time of a fully wound reel of tape, buffer reservoirs of tape are provided to allow high acceleration of the tape at the head assembly. To maintain the average rate of tape transfer equal throughout the system, the motion of the reels is controlled by the length of tape in the reservoirs.

The component parts of a typical tape transport mechanism are illustrated in Fig. 4.8. The tape passes over two capstans, rotating in opposite directions at a constant speed, and is held in contact with the head assembly, which is usually mounted between the capstans as shown. When the tape is transferred from the right-hand to the left-hand reel, for example, the pinch roller is brought into contact with the tape as it passes over the left-hand capstan, causing the tape to move from right to left. When enough tape has been withdrawn from the reservoir on the right to allow the light from the lamp to fall on the top photo-electric cell, the motor driving the right-hand reel is operated to unwind the tape into the box. Similarly, when enough tape has been fed into the

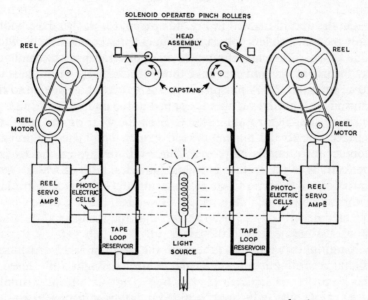

FIG. 4.8 *Typical magnetic-tape transport mechanism*

reservoir on the left to interrupt the light to the lower photo-cell, the motor operates to wind tape on to the left-hand reel. By applying a partial vacuum to the bottom of the boxes, the tape loops are forced down into the reservoirs and sufficient tension is provided for accurate spooling of the tape on the reels.

In some vacuum-reservoir boxes, the light source and photo-electric cells, controlling the motion of the reels, are replaced by pressure sensitive switches. The reservoir of tape is provided by a system of arms, springs and jockey rollers in some units where the motion of the reels is controlled by the position of the arms. Since the length of tape which must be held in the reservoir increases with tape speed, in high-speed units the size of the vacuum reservoir may become embarrassing. This problem has been solved in one equipment, by using a bin into which the tape is thrown by its own momentum. When the bin is only slightly wider than the tape, the tape forms itself into loose folds and can easily be extracted without tangling. An elegant method of determining the quantity of tape in the bin involves sensing the change in capacitance between the front and back plates of the bin, as the dielectric constant changes with the quantity of tape in the bin.

On the unit illustrated in Fig. 4.8, except for the head assembly, only the pinch rollers come into contact with the magnetic surface. The pinch rollers are eliminated in some transport mechanisms by the use of vacuum capstans, thus reducing wear on the surface to a minimum.[19,20] Atmospheric pressure forces the tape on to the capstan as a partial vacuum is applied to the underside of the tape through slots in a rotating sleeve. Even the wear on the magnetic surface due to the magnetic head can be eliminated, if out-of-contact recording is employed. Since failures are caused by imperfections in the surface and dust particles, both of which cause variations in the head-to-surface spacing, out-of-contact recording reduces failures due to this cause, although at the cost of decreased packing density. It has been shown that the read-signal obtained from a sinusoidal recording falls off at 55 db per wavelength separation between the tape and the reading head. Although digital recording is not sinusoidal, a similar relationship holds.[23] To keep the magnetic surface as free as possible from dust particles, most tape units are contained in a pressurized cabinet.

4.3.2 TAPE ACCESS ARRANGEMENTS

In normal practice, the recording system used with magnetic tape is very similar to parallel operation of a magnetic drum. A synchronizing waveform or clock is recorded on a separate track but, whereas the clock is pre-recorded on a drum, on tape it is usually re-recorded simultaneously with the information tracks during each writing operation. Because of the time taken to accelerate and decelerate the tape, information is written or read in blocks, each of which contains hundreds of words and is marked and labelled at its start. Block marks are usually recorded on a separate track while the labels are recorded on the data tracks at the beginning of a block. To avoid overwriting block marks and labels, writing is inhibited on the block-mark channel during normal operation and the detection of a block mark always switches the system to the read mode until the label has been read. The required block of data can then be found by reading the next block label on the tape and computing how many blocks forward or back the tape must be moved. During the searching process, the block marks are sensed and counted, until the tape has moved through the correct number of blocks. The next block label can then be read to ensure that the required block has been reached and the information transferred to or from the tape. In most data-processing systems, this search can be carried out simultaneously with other operations and this reduces the effective access time to the tape.

Since information recorded on magnetic tape may not be read for some time, the delay in discovering any errors which might have occurred during writing could have serious consequences. For this reason, in addition to the usual parity checks which are applied, it is essential to check a block immediately after writing. This is often carried out by computing the sum of all the words in the block and recording this sum after the data. When the information is read, the sum check is again computed and compared with the recorded sum check. If a common read/write head is employed, this check after writing involves reversing the tape to the beginning of the block and then reading the block. The three passes of the tape which this requires can be reduced to one if a separate read-head, trailing the write-head, is used. Here the block is written and checked on a single pass of the tape.

The information transfer rate from a magnetic tape depends on the tape velocity, packing density and the number of parallel tracks on the tape. The number of tracks per unit width is determined by the same factors which determine the track density on a drum but about twenty tracks per inch is common practice. Up to 4-in. wide tape has been used, but in data-processing applications 1-in. tape is most common. Increasing tape velocity causes increased frictional wear on the surface and the heads, as well as making it more difficult to maintain the tape in contact and alignment with the head assembly. Although a velocity of 200 in. per second is in use on at least one equipment, most high-performance units employ either 120 or 150 in. per second. The factors limiting packing density are dealt with in the section on High-Density Recording.

Before information can be read or recorded reliably, the tape must be moving with a nearly constant velocity. The tape which passes under the head during acceleration or deceleration cannot therefore be used for storage and the length of tape so lost may become significant at high tape velocities. To reduce tape wastage the minimum length of tape traversed in one pass may be increased by increasing the number of words in one block. In addition, starting and stopping times must be minimized in the design of the tape transport mechanism and times less than 2 milliseconds have been achieved.

4.3.3. HIGH-DENSITY RECORDING

In addition to the factors limiting packing density, common to all magnetic-surface recording, namely, element demagnetization and read-head resolution, magnetic-tape systems suffer from the effect of tape skew. This effect is illustrated in Fig. 4.9 where the misalignment of the tape is exaggerated. Skew is caused by many factors, including inaccurate slitting of the tape so that its width varies, by variations in tape thickness causing non-simultaneous clutching of the tape on the capstan and by the tape guiding arrangements. Element demagnetization is not normally a limiting factor and, with a well-designed reading head, over 2000 flux reversals per inch can be resolved. When the tape is skewed with respect to the head, the elements in the different tracks across the tape do not pass the head simultaneously as can be seen in Fig. 4.9. When this phase variation across the tape is a significant fraction of a digit period, the same clock track cannot be used with all the information tracks.

If the packing density in a recording system is not to be skew-limited, each track or channel must contain its own synchronizing information. This can be provided by inserting synchronizing pulses periodically in the recorded waveform. These pulses can then be extracted and used to control the channel clock but their extraction leads to some complication in the equipment required. If the recorded pattern contains at least one flux reversal per digit, as in phase modulation recording, timing information can be extracted from the information signal itself. Three methods of recording which are self-clocking are shown in Fig. 4.10. The first is the standard PM method in which the flux reversal in the centre of the digit cell is either positive for 1 or negative for 0. The second is really a form of frequency modulation in which 1 is represented by one cycle of a square wave at the digit frequency and 0 by one half-cycle of a square wave at half of the digit frequency. In the third, the modified non-return-to-zero, 1 is represented by a positive flux transition at the beginning of the digit cell, while 0 is represented by a negative flux reversal; when two

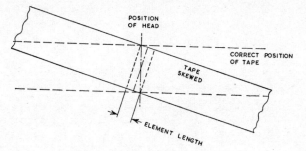

FIG. 4.9 *Effect of tape skew*

similar digits occur sequentially, an extra flux reversal must be introduced in the centre of the cell. From Fig. 4.10 it will be seen that all the recorded flux patterns consist of complete cycles at the digit frequency or half-cycles at half the digit frequency: for example, PM and modified NRZ are identical but for a phase shift

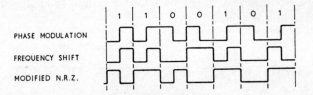

FIG. 4.10 *Methods of self-clocking recording*

of half a digit period. Figure 4.11 shows the waveforms in one method of recovering the information from a PM recording. The signal from the read-head is amplified and limited before differentiation and full-wave rectification. This results in a train of pulses which occur at the points where the read signal changes sign, and which synchronize the clock generator. The recorded information is now recovered by gating the read signal, after limiting, with the synchronized clock.

If the digits of a character are recorded in parallel tracks on the

tape, a 'de-skewing' buffer is required to correct the time-displace-
ment in the reading of the digits of a character, which occurs
because of tape skew. Recording densities up to 500 or 600 bits
per inch have been utilized with separate clock channels, while,
with self-clocking recording systems, densities up to 1500 bits per
inch are in use and even higher densities appear feasible.[28] This

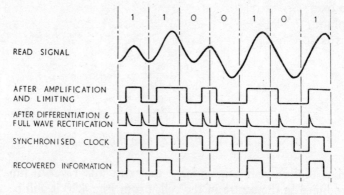

FIG. 4.11 *Waveforms in a method of recovering the
information from a PM recording*

increase in recording density is achieved at the cost of considerably
increased complexity in the hardware required for recovering the
recorded information.

4.4 FILE STORES USING MAGNETIC-SURFACE RECORDING

Considerable effort has gone into the development of storage
systems with the capacity of magnetic tape but without its disadvantage of long access time. One of the first systems developed[30]
employs fifty separate lengths of tape, each 250 ft long. The tapes
are stored in separate boxes and guided, side by side, over a
system of drive rollers which is common to all the tapes. A head
carriage runs on a track under the tapes and can be positioned
under the selected tape which is then driven by a solenoid-operated
pinch-roller mounted on the head carriage. The capacity of this
system is 22×10^6 bits and the average access time is 14 sec.

Several systems have been developed using magnetic coated discs. Single discs have been employed in place of magnetic drums as the high-speed store in some early digital computers. One of the first multi-disc[31,32] units for large-capacity file storage is constructed of fifty rotating discs, each side of which has 200 concentric tracks storing 4000 bits per track. The discs, 24 in. in diameter, are constructed of 0·1 in. thick aluminium, coated with iron oxide and are mounted on a vertical shaft, rotating at 1200 revolutions per minute. Access to the information stored on the discs is gained by moving an arm vertically to the selected disc

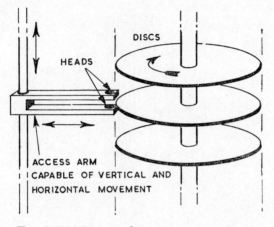

FIG. 4.12 *Magnetic-disc access arrangements*

and then radially to the selected track. Two magnetic heads, one for the under and one for the top surface, are mounted on the arm which is bifurcated to allow the selected disc to rotate between the heads, as shown in Fig. 4.12. The head-to-surface spacing is maintained at 0·001 in. by an air bearing obtained from small jets round the head. The capacity of the system is 80×10^6 bits and the maximum access time is 0·8 sec., with an average of 0·15 sec. Other multi-disc systems are available in which the access time is reduced by each disc having individual heads mounted on separate arms so that only the radial motion to the selected track is required.[38]

In other systems, the magnetic surface is in the form of cards which are assembled in a stack or magazine. The selected card is extracted from the stack and fed to a mechanism which moves it past the read- and write-heads. In one ingenious mechanism,[36] 256 cards, each 14 in. long by $3\frac{1}{4}$ in. wide, are suspended from eight rods which are engaged in notches in the cards. These rods have two positions, one of which holds the card while the other allows it to drop freely. The notches on the cards are binary coded, so that only one card is completely free to drop for each of the 256 possible combinations of the positions of the eight rods. When the selected card drops, it is guided on to a rotating drum to which a partial vacuum is applied. The card is therefore held on the drum's

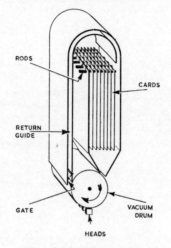

FIG. 4.13 *Magnetic-card access arrangement*

surface by atmospheric pressure and, after acceleration to the peripheral velocity of the drum, 400 in. per second, it passes a set of read- and write-heads. After the information is read or recorded, the card may be held on the drum for re-access to the information or it may be removed and returned to the magazine. A two-position gate either leaves the card unaffected on the drum or strips it from the surface into the return guide as shown in Fig. 4.13. The unaided momentum of the card ensures its return to the magazine, in which the order of the cards is unimportant. Each card has seven tracks, each containing a maximum of 3100 six-bit characters. A recording density of 250 bits per inch gives a transfer rate of 10^5 characters per second and the access time to any block of information is less than 0·2 sec.

4.5 READING AND WRITING ON A MAGNETIC SURFACE BY MEANS OF AN ELECTRON BEAM

Patterns recorded on a magnetic surface can be detected using the techniques of electron-mirror microscopy. The deflection of an electron beam by the field of a magnetized surface near which it passes can be utilized to reproduce the pattern of magnetization on the surface, either optically or electrically. The inherent resolution of this method of reading is very high and, since the beam has little inertia, information can be read at a very high rate. The equipment is rather complex and the system suffers from the severe disadvantage of requiring the magnetic surface to be in an evacuated enclosure during reading.

If a small area of a magnetic surface, which is uniformly magnetized in a direction normal to the surface, is heated to a temperature above the Curie point, the area becomes non-magnetic. Due to the flux closure which takes place through it when non-magnetic, on cooling this area becomes magnetized in the opposite direction to the surrounding surface. The local heating due to the dissipation energy of an electron beam can thus be used to record information at a very high density. It has been estimated that a density of 10^5 bits per square centimetre is possible and that writing speeds up to 10^6 bits per second may be attained.[40] An intermetallic compound of manganese and bismuth has been used as the magnetic surface but there are difficult problems which have yet to be solved in the preparation of the material.

4.6 MAGNETO-OPTICAL READ-OUT OF MAGNETIC RECORDING

The use of the Kerr magneto–optic effect has been proposed as a means of reading magnetic records with increased resolution over conventional magnetic read-heads. When light is reflected from a surface which is magnetized, the plane of polarization of the reflected light is rotated with respect to the plane of polarization of the incident light. Since the direction of this rotation depends on the direction of magnetization, this Kerr effect may be used to detect the pattern of magnetization on the surface. Because of head and surface wear at the high speeds involved, out-of-contact heads are employed in drum or disc systems and the separation between head and surface necessarily reduces the maximum packing density. Magneto-optical read-out does not involve mechanical contact with the surface and should therefore allow the maximum packing density to be realized. The system requires the magnetic surface to have a high and uniform reflection coefficient for the incident light and, hence, only metallic recording surfaces are suitable. Experiments have shown that densities over 2000 bits per inch may be detected, using a specially developed magnetic surface.[43]

BIBLIOGRAPHY

GENERAL

1. Williams, F. C., Kilburn, T. and Thomas, G. E. 'Universal High-speed Digital Computers: A Magnetic Store', *Proc. I.E.E.*, **99**, Part II, pp. 94–106 (1952).

2. Lubkin, S. 'An Improved Reading System for Magnetically Recorded Digital Data', *I.R.E. Trans. on Electronic Computers*, EC–3, pp. 22–5 (1954).

3. Hoagland, A. S. 'A Logical Reading System for Non-Return-to-Zero Magnetic Recording', *I.R.E. Trans. on Electronic Computers*, EC–4, pp. 93–5 (1955).

4. Hoagland, A. S. 'Magnetic Recording Head Design', *Proc. Western Joint Computer Conference.* San Francisco, Feb. 1956, pp. 26–31.

5. Ball, A. G., Wright, J. E., Hood, D. L. and Butcher, J. A. W. 'The Design of Recording Heads for Use on a Magnetic Storage Drum and the Characteristics of Various Recording Surfaces', *Proc. I.E.E.*, **109**, Part B, Supplement No. 21, pp. 165–74 (1962).

6. Kilburn, T., Hoffman, G. R. and Wolstenholme, P. 'Reading of Magnetic Records by Reluctance Variation', *Proc. I.E.E.*, **103**, Part B, Supplement No. 2, pp. 333–6 (1956).

7. Kerr, D. and Quirk, E. J. M. 'A Magnetic Read Head with Output Independent of Tape Speed', *Jour. Brit. I.R.E.*, **20**, pp. 743–8 (1960).

8. Johnson, H. A. 'A Multi-Channel Transducer for Magnetic Recording', *I.R.E. National Convention Record*, 1957, **5**, Part 7, pp. 130–4.

MAGNETIC DRUMS

9. Booth, A. D. 'A Magnetic Digital Storage System', *Electronic Engineering*, **21**, pp. 234–8 (1949).

10. Claydon, D. O., Page, J. J. and Osborne, C. F. 'The Magnetic Storage Drum on the ACE Pilot Model', *Proc. I.E.E.*, **103**, Part B, Supplement No. 3, pp. 509–14 (1956).

11. Williams, F. C. and West, J. C. 'Position Sychronization of a Rotating Drum', *Proc. I.E.E.*, **98**, Part II, pp. 29–34 (1951).

12. Majumdar, D. D. 'On the Optimum Design of Magnetic Drum Stores', *Jour. Inst. Telecommunication Engineers* (New Delhi), **5**, pp. 211–22 (1959).

13. May, M., Miller, G. T., Howard, R. A., and Shifran, G. A. 'A High-speed Small-size Magnetic Drum Memory Unit for Subminiature Computers', *Proc. Eastern Joint Computer Conference*, Dec. 1959, pp. 190–9.

14. Turner, K. I. and Thompson, J. E. 'The Magnetic Drum Store of the MERCURY Computer', *Electronic Engineering*, **32**, pp. 16–21 (1960).

15. Knight, L. and Circuit, M. P. 'A High-Density File Drum as a Computer Store', *Jour. Brit. I.R.E.*, **20**, pp. 41–5 (1960).

16. Schaffer, R. R. and Gill, D. W. 'Design and Operation of a High-speed Increased-capacity Magnetic Drum', *I.R.E. National Convention Record*, 1961, **9**, Part 2, pp. 128–31.

MAGNETIC TAPE

17. Buslik, W. S. 'IBM Magnetic Tape Reader and Recorder', *Proc. Joint Computer Conference* held at New York, Dec. 1952, pp. 89–90.

18. Welsh, H. F., and Lukoff, H. 'The UNISERVO—Tape Reader and Recorder', *Proc. Joint Computer Conference* held at New York, Dec., 1952, pp. 47–53.

19. Wilkes, M. V. and Willis, D. W. 'A Magnetic Tape Auxiliary Storage System for the EDSAC', *Proc. I.E.E.*, **103**, Part B, Supplement No. 2, pp. 337–45 (1956).

20. Willard, D. W. 'A Large-scale Error-Correcting Tape Memory System'. Paper presented at the I.F.I.P. Congress, 1962, held in Munich, Sept. 1962. Proceedings to be published by the North Holland Publishing Co., Amsterdam.

21. Lawrance, R. B. 'An Advanced Magnetic Tape System for Data Processing', *Proc. Eastern Joint Computer Conference*, Dec. 1959, pp. 181–9.

22. Mee, C. D. 'Magnetic Tape for Data Recording', *Proc. I.E.E.*, **105**, Part B, pp. 373–82 (1958).

23. Noble, R. 'The Assessment of the Reliability of Magnetic Tape for Data Processing', *Jour. Brit. I.R.E.*, **20**, pp. 737–42 (1960).

24. Franklin, D. P. 'Factors Influencing the Application of Magnetic Tape Recording to Digital Computers', *Jour. Brit. I.R.E.*, **20**, pp. 9–21 (1960).

25. Willis, D. W. and Skinner, P. 'Some Engineering Aspects of Magnetic Tape System Design', *Jour. Brit., I.R.E.*, **20**, pp. 867–76 (1960).

HIGH-DENSITY RECORDING

26. Hoagland, A. S. and Bacon, G. C. 'High-Density Digital Magnetic Recording Techniques', *Trans. I.R.E. on Electronic Computers*, EC–9, pp. 2–11 (1960): also published in *Proc. I.R.E.*, **49**, pp. 258–67 (1961).

27. Batsel, C. N. Jnr., and Ross, W. L. 'High-density Digital Magnetic Tape Recording', *I.R.E. Western Electronic Show and Convention Record*, 1961. Paper No. 13/2.

28. 'High Density Recording Comes of Age', *Automatic Control*. Dec. 1961.

29. Ziman, G. C. 'Maximum Pulse-Packing Densities on Magnetic Tape', *Electronic Engineering*, **34**, pp. 521–5 (1962).

FILE STORES

30. Macdonald, D. N. 'DATAFILE—A New Tool for Extensive File Storage', *Proc. Eastern Joint Computer Conference*, Dec. 1956, pp. 124–8.

31. Noyes, T. and Dickenson, W. E. 'Engineering Design of a Magnetic-disc Random-access Memory', *Proc. Western Joint Computer Conference*, Feb. 1956, pp. 42–4.

32. Glover, A. C. 'A Magnetic Disc Random-access Memory', *Jour. Brit. I.R.E.*, **20**, pp. 22–4 (1960).

33. Hoagland, A. S. 'A High Track-density Servo-access System for Magnetic Recording Disc Storage', *I.B.M. Journal of Research and Development*, **5**, pp. 287–96 (1961).

34. Rabinow, J. 'The Notched-disc Memory', *Electrical Engineering*, **71**, pp. 745–9 (1952).

35. Hayes, R. M. and Wiener, J. 'MAGNACARD—A New Concept in Data Handling', *I.R.E.*, 1957, *Wescon Convention Record*, Part 4, pp. 205–10.

36. Bloom, L., Pardo, I., Keating, W. and Mayne, E. 'Card Random Access Memory (CRAM): Functions and Use', *Proc. 1961 Eastern Joint Computer Conference*, pp. 147–57, Macmillan (New York 1962).

37. Hoagland, A. S. 'Mass Storage' (Review of File Storage Systems), *Proc. I.R.E.*, **50**, pp. 1087–92 (1962).

38. McLaughlin, H. J. 'Disc File Memories', *Instr. Control Systems*, **34**, pp. 2063–8 (1961).

READING AND WRITING WITH ELECTRON BEAM

39. Mayer, L. 'Electron Mirror Microscopy of Patterns Recorded on Magnetic Tape', *Jour. Applied Physics*, **29**, pp. 658–60 (1958).

40. Mayer, L. 'Magnetic Writing with an Electron Beam', *Jour. of Applied Physics*, **29**, pp. 1454–6 (1958).

41. Freundlich, M. M., Begun, S. J., Breitzer, D. I., Gehman, J. B. and Lewis, J. K. 'Experiments in Magnetic Tape Readout with an Electron Beam', *Proc. I.R.E.*, **49**, pp. 498–509 (1961).

MAGNETO-OPTICAL READ-OUT OF MAGNETIC RECORDING

42. Lentz, T. and Miyata, J. 'Magneto-Optical Readout of Magnetic Recording', *Electronics*, **34**, pp. 36–9 (Sept. 1st, 1961).

43. Miyata, J. and Lentz, T. 'MAGOP—A New Approach to High-density Digital Magnetic Recording', *Large-Capacity Memory Techniques for Computing Systems*, edited by M. C. Yovits, pp. 117–34. Macmillan and Co. (New York, 1962).

CHAPTER 5

MAGNETIC-CORE STORAGE

ALTHOUGH any ferromagnet with hysteresis can be used to store a binary digit, 0 and 1 being represented by the two remanent states of magnetization as illustrated in Fig. 5.1(a), gaining access to the stored information remains a problem which must be solved economically. It is possible to devise a storage system in which each ferromagnet is associated with some other non-linear element, such as a diode, which is used for access. Since one ferromagnet and at least one diode are required for each binary digit stored, such a system is not economic for large capacities. When the hysteresis loop has a rectangular shape, as shown in Fig. 5.1(b) the non-linearity necessary for access is inherent in the BH characteristic. Each ferromagnet can now be used for selection as well as storage, and large-capacity systems become feasible. To be suitable for use in such a storage system, a ferro-magnetic material must possess the property that the state of magnetization is not materially affected by the application of a field of $\frac{1}{2}H_m$, while a field of H_m will almost completely reverse the magnetization, as shown in Fig. 5.1(b). Self-demagnetizing effects are avoided when the material forms a closed magnetic path and the most convenient shape is the anchor-ring or torus, which is commonly referred to as a magnetic core.

The above property makes it possible to select one magnetic core from an array of the form illustrated in Fig. 5.2. If a current of $\frac{1}{2}I_m$, corresponding to a field in the core of $\frac{1}{2}H_m$, is turned on in one X coordinate wire threading one column of the array and a similar current in one Y coordinate wire threading one row, then the core common to both the selected row and column will have a field of H_m applied which, if the core is initially in the remanent state corresponding to 1, is sufficient to reverse the magnetization to the 0 state. The other cores on the selected row and column,

70

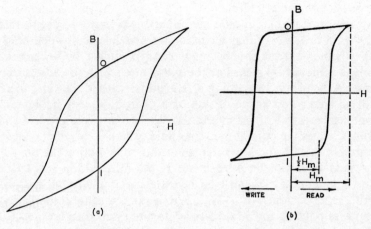

(a) normal   (b) rectangular

FIG. 5.1 *Ferromagnetic hysteresis loops*

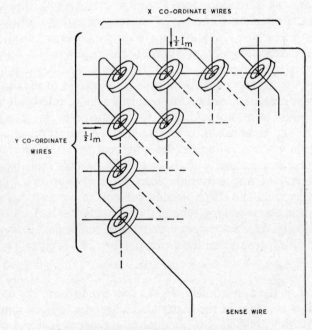

FIG. 5.2 *Storage array of magnetic cores*

F

however, are subjected to a field of $\frac{1}{2}H_m$ only, which is insufficient to cause any change in their state. Having selected a core in this way its initial state of magnetization may be detected by determining whether or not a substantial change of flux has occurred. This is achieved by means of the sense wire which threads all the cores in the array. Depending on the initial state of the core, there will be either no change of flux or a change corresponding to a complete reversal of magnetization. Since the reading operation always leaves the core in the same state, which is usually taken to represent 0, with the large change of flux representing the digit 1, the read operation is destructive. If the information has to be stored indefinitely, it must be rewritten after each read-out. To write a 1, currents of $-\frac{1}{2}I_m$, that is, of equal amplitude but opposite polarity to the read-currents, are applied to the selected X and Y coordinate wires, causing the selected core to be switched to the 1 state.

This two-coordinate or *coincident-current* selection scheme makes it possible to employ an array of rectangular-hysteresis loop cores as a random-access storage system with destructive read-out. By selecting one out of m X wires and one out of n Y wires, say, one core from an array of $m \times n$ cores can be selected.

The use of rectangular-loop cores for storage was first described in a paper by Forrester in 1951.[1] This work was based on cores made of several wraps of metal tape. In addition to the difficulty of fabrication, these early cores required tens of microseconds to switch and were not suitable for high-speed, large-capacity systems. The time taken to reverse the magnetization of a rectangular-loop core is limited by eddy currents in the material and by the finite velocity of the magnetic domain walls by which the reversal of magnetization takes place. When metal tape is made very thin, the effect of eddy currents is reduced to insignificance and the switching time is then determined by the domain-wall velocity. This velocity is proportional to the field in excess of the coercive force so that the switching time, T_s, is given by

$$T_s = \tau H_c/(H_o - H_c)$$

where H_o is the applied field, H_c the coercive force of the material and τ is a constant of the material. The product τH_c is known as the switching coefficient of the material. Since coincident-current operation limits the applied field to less than $2H_c$, the switching time cannot be decreased by increasing the applied field.

In 1950 research into ferrite materials, based on the magnetic iron oxide or magnetite of the lode stone, led to a magnesium manganese ferrite which showed a rectangular-hysteresis loop. The potential of this material was recognized by the workers at the Massachusetts Institute of Technology and further research and development resulted in the production of ferrite cores.[5] These were incorporated in the first core store put into operation in the WHIRLWIND computer at M.I.T. early in 1953. The non-metallic ferrite, with its high resistivity, removed the eddy-current limitation to switching speed. In addition, it was found that the intrinsic switching speed of ferrite cores was higher than that of the metal-tape cores, switching times just greater than one micro-second being obtainable under coincident-current operation. It has been found that the switching coefficient is of the same order for all ferrite materials so far investigated. Higher switching speeds, therefore, can only be achieved by increasing the coercive force, resulting in a corresponding increase in the drive current required. Materials which switch in less than 0·5 microsecond are now available.

The first ferrite cores had an external diameter of 0·08 in. (2 mm) and an internal diameter of 0·05 in. (1·3 mm). Improved manufacturing and assembly techniques have led to the wide-spread use of cores with an 0·05 in. (1·3 mm) external and 0·03 in. (0·75 mm) internal diameter, and cores of 0·03 in. (0·75 mm) external diameter are now also available. Since the rule for successive reductions in size appears to be that each new core must fit inside its predecessor, perhaps the next core to be available will be one with an external diameter of 0·018 in. (0·46 mm). There is certainly no difficulty in manufacturing such cores, although the handling problems become severe as the size is reduced. Ferrite cores are manufactured by moulding under pressure the dry constituents mixed with an organic binding material and firing the mixture at an elevated temperature where sintering takes place. The advantages of small cores are reduced driving current, which is proportional to the diameter, and reduced energy loss due to hysteresis.

5.1 ACCESS ARRANGEMENTS

There are two basic arrangements of magnetic-core stores, for parallel operation, the two-coordinate selection or bit-organized arrangement, also known as the M.I.T. or coincident-current system (the latter name is misleading since all core stores depend for their operation on current-coincidence in two or more wires),

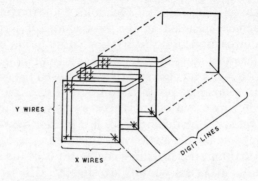

FIG. 5.3 *Three-dimensional core array*

and the direct selection or word-organized arrangement. In the first system, planes are stacked and connected in the three-dimensional array shown in Fig. 5.3. Each core in a plane is threaded by

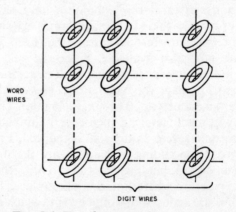

FIG. 5.4 *Two-dimensional core array*

one X, one Y and a common Z or digit wire, corresponding to the sense wire in Fig. 5.2. The application of half-read currents to one X and one Y wire selects corresponding cores on each plane and the information stored is read out in parallel on the digit wires. In the word-organized system the cores are arranged in a two-dimensional array as shown in Fig. 5.4. Here the application of the read-current in one word wire selects all the cores in the word and again the information is read out in parallel on the digit lines. It should be noted that the number of coordinates needed to select a core when reading is always one less than the number needed when writing; this extra input during writing determines whether the core is set to the 1 or 0 state. For example, the reading operation does not require current-coincidence in a word-organized system but the writing operation does require coincidence of currents applied to the word and digit lines. To assess the advantages and limitations of these two systems a more detailed description of their operation is given below.

5.1.1 TWO-COORDINATE SELECTION SYSTEM

The threading arrangements of the cores in a typical four-wire plane are shown in more detail in Fig. 5.5. In addition to the X and Y wires each core is threaded by the common sense and inhibit wires. The state of a selected core is read out by applying currents to the X and Y wires common to the core and sensing the e.m.f. proportional to the rate of change of flux induced in the sense wire. The X and Y drive wires are connected in series for all planes as shown in Fig. 5.3 so that corresponding cores in each plane are selected simultaneously and the output signals appear in parallel on all the sense wires. To write a 1 into the core, the currents in the X and Y wires are reversed and the core is switched to the remanent state corresponding to a stored 1. When it is required to write a 0 into the core, an inhibit current, equal in amplitude to but opposing the X and Y write-currents, is applied to the inhibit wire, thus inhibiting the core from switching. Typical read- and write-currents are shown in Fig. 5.6 together with the output voltages induced in the sense line.

5.1.2 NOISE IN THE TWO-COORDINATE SELECTION SYSTEM

Since the hysteresis loop of the cores is not ideal, in each core on the selected X and Y coordinates, the current of $\frac{1}{2}I$ causes a change of flux which contributes to the output e.m.f. on the sense wire. The 'noise' voltage from one core is an appreciable fraction of the output voltage for a 1, which would therefore be swamped in all but the smallest arrays. To reduce the effect of these noise voltages, the sense wire is arranged to thread alternate cores on the X and Y wires, in opposite polarity so that the noise voltages

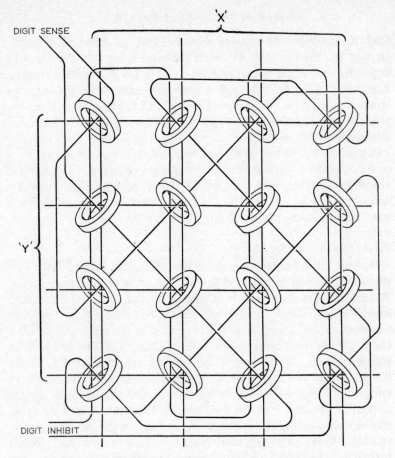

FIG. 5.5 *Threading of cores in a four-wire plane*

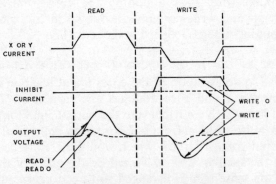

FIG. 5.6 *Waveforms in two-dimensional selection plane*

tend to cancel.[5] Cancellation is not perfect, however, since the change in flux in each core subjected to the $\frac{1}{2}I$ disturb current depends on the previous history of the core. Typical minor hysteresis loops for such disturbances are shown in Fig. 5.7. After reading, the state of magnetization of the core will be at point A on the flux/current hysteresis loop, corresponding to an undisturbed 0, usually written uV_z; after writing a 1 into the core, its state will be at point D, corresponding to an undisturbed 1, or uV_1. A half-current in the read direction in the case of a stored 1 will move the state of the core to point E, corresponding to a disturbed 1, or dV_1. Further disturb pulses in the same direction have little effect on the state of the core which remains very close to this point. A disturb pulse in the write direction will now move the remanent point to F, from which another read-disturb pulse will return the core to E. Similarly the remanent point for a stored 0 will alternate between B and C, depending on whether the core was last write- or read-disturbed respectively. The degree to which cancellation can be effected between two cores depends on the remanent points from which they start when a read-disturb current is applied. Although the largest flux change occurs when a core storing a 1 is read-disturbed, that is, from D to E, there can be only one core on any row or column at the undisturbed remanent point, D. Since reading must occur before writing, the operation of writing 1 into a core necessarily involves read-disturbing all the cores on the same row and column. The worst case occurs when both the information stored in the cores and the last disturbance to which they were subjected are dissimilar; that is, when the cores are storing 1 and 0 respectively and when one core has been write-disturbed and the other read-disturbed. In this case one core will start from B and end up at C while the other both starts from and returns to E. The resultant output from a pair of cores, due to imperfect cancellation, is often called the 'delta' voltage and is a limiting factor determining the size of an array.

The delta voltage occurs mainly during the rise-time of the applied current pulse since it is not subject to the same delay which occurs when a core is switched. Figure 5.8 shows how the output voltage from a core storing a 1 occurs later than the typical delta voltage, and that it is therefore possible to greatly increase the discrimination by sampling the voltage on the sense wire after the delta voltage has decayed.[5]

Several other methods can be employed to reduce the effect of

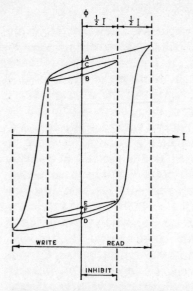

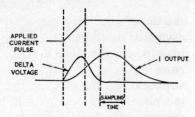

FIG. 5.8 *Time discrimination between wanted and unwanted outputs from a two-dimensional array*

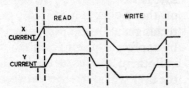

FIG. 5.7 *Minor hysteresis loops for core in two-dimensional array*

FIG. 5.9 *Reduction of noise by staggering drive currents*

FIG. 5.10 *Reduction of noise by subdivision of array into sub-arrays*

the delta noise in large arrays. Since one cause of this is the asymmetrical disturb condition on pairs of cores, the introduction of a 'post-write disturb' pulse on the inhibit wire always leaves pairs similarly disturbed and greatly reduces the effect.[17] When writing 0, the normal inhibit pulse read-disturbs all the cores in the plane, so that it is only necessary to apply the post-write disturb after writing 1. A second method which can be used is to delay the application of the current in one coordinate wire with respect to the current in the other wire as shown in Fig. 5.9. The delta voltage now occurs in two parts, the first when the X current, say, is turned on and so only the second part, on the application of the Y current, reduces the discrimination. If the array is rectangular rather than square a further reduction can be obtained by applying the current in the longer coordinate first.

Both of the above methods of delta noise reduction increase the cycle time, the first by the time taken by the post-write disturb pulse, which, it should be noted, need not be as long as the normal current pulses, and the second by the delay introduced between the X and Y drive currents. One method which does not increase the cycle time is to divide the sense wire into sections, of which only the one containing the selected core is gated to the digit circuits.[13] Figure 5.10 shows an example of this method in which the sense wire is divided into four sub-arrays. The diagonally opposite quarters of the sense wire are connected in series dividing the sense wire into two sections. With this arrangement only the noise from half the total number of disturbed cores in the array appears on the sense wire with the signal, since the noise from the other two quadrants, which are half-selected, appears on the other sense wire.

5.1.3 WORD-ORGANIZED SYSTEM

The major advantage of direct selection is the elimination of all half-current disturbances from the system during reading, since only the cores in the selected word are subjected to the full write-current. The price which has to be paid for this immunity from half-select noise is some extra equipment in the selection circuits. While in the bit-organized system it is necessary to select one out of n wires on two coordinates to gain access to one word out of n^2, in the word-organized system, one out of n^2 wires must be selected. To read one word in the system of Fig. 5.4, a read-current in the selected wire switches all the cores in the word to the 0 state, causing a large e.m.f. to appear on the digit wires threading those cores which had contained 1. Writing into the store still requires current-coincidence between a write half-current flowing in the word wire in the opposite direction to the read-current, and a similar augmenting current flowing in the digit wires threading the cores into which 1 has to be written. An alternative mode of writing is possible in which a full write-current is applied to the word wire and an inhibiting half-current of opposite polarity in the digit wires threading those cores into which 0 has to be written.

During reading, although there is no output from half-selected cores, the flux change in the cores does depend on the number of disturbances due to currents on the digit lines. In the case where the digit current augments the word current, all the disturbances are in the write direction and, therefore, only cores on the digit line which are storing 0 are affected. In the inhibiting case, all the disturbances are in the read direction and only affect cores storing 1. The worst discrimination, in the first case, is between an undisturbed 1 and a many-times write-disturbed 0 while in the second, between a many-times disturbed 1 and an undisturbed 0. If the core characteristics are such that its remanent state is changed appreciably by disturb pulses after the first, the effect of disturbances can be reduced by employing unequal word and digit currents. Since there can never be more than one disturbance due to the word current, while there may be an unlimited number due to the digit current, decreasing the digit current and increasing the word current by the same amount to keep the write-current constant, may increase the discrimination.[20]

Since the reading operation does not rely on current-coincidence, there is no limit to the amplitude of the read-current. As the switching time decreases with an increase in applied field, the duration of the read-phase may be reduced by asymmetrical operation in which unequal read- and write-currents are employed. The write-phase can also be speeded up by using a 3 : 1 selection ratio in which the applied write-current can be increased by half as much again. This is achieved by applying augmenting digit currents, of $\frac{1}{2}I_m$ to the digits storing 1 and inhibiting currents, of $-\frac{1}{2}I_m$ to the digits storing 0, while a full write-current is applied to the word line. A current of $\frac{3}{2}I_m$ is applied to the cores which therefore switch in about half the time required for 2 : 1 selection, while the disturbing current is still limited to $\frac{1}{2}I_m$.

5.1.4 3 : 1 SELECTION ARRANGEMENTS

Other arrangements are possible in which the selection ratio, that is, the ratio of the field applied to the selected core to the field applied to an unselected core, is higher than the usual 2 : 1. For example, in the array of Fig. 5.5, if a current of $-\frac{1}{3}I_m$ flows in the inhibit winding and currents of $+\frac{2}{3}I_m$ in the selected X and Y coordinates, the selected core is subjected to a current equal to I_m. Since the unselected cores on the selected coordinates are only subjected to a current of $+\frac{1}{3}I_m$ and all the remaining cores to $-\frac{1}{3}I_m$, the resulting 3 : 1 selection ratio reduces the effect of the selection currents on partially selected cores. If the currents are increased to $-\frac{1}{2}I_m$ and I_m the selected core can be over-driven by $\frac{3}{2}I_m$ and the switching time decreased. An alternative method of obtaining a 3 : 1 selection ratio in the array of Fig. 5.5 is to apply $\frac{3}{4}I_m$ to the selected X and Y coordinates and $-\frac{1}{4}I_m$ to the unselected coordinates. The price which has to be paid for this increase in selection ratio is increased complexity of the driving circuits which must now be able to supply currents of different amplitude and polarity. In addition 3 : 1 selection systems have only limited application, since they cannot be applied to the three-dimensional system of Fig. 5.3, because the parallel operation requires inhibit currents in the planes into which 0 has to be written.

5.1.5 MULTIPLE-COINCIDENCE ARRAYS

Since the switching time of a ferrite core decreases as the applied field increases, systems which give a higher selection ratio than the usual 2 : 1 can be employed to give higher speed operation. Multiple-coincidence schemes in which more than two coordinates are selected can give a considerable increase in selection ratio. The array of four cores in Fig. 5.11 is a three-coordinate selection system which gives an infinite selection ratio. If currents of $2I_m$ flow in the selected coordinates and $-I_m$ in the unselected coordinates, the selected core is linked by a total current of $6I_m$ while the net current linking the others is zero. Although with arrays larger than 2×2 it is impossible to achieve an infinite selection ratio using only three coordinates, an improvement to 5 : 1 is possible in an array of arbitrary size. For example, the array shown in Fig. 5.12 is a three-coordinate system which gives a 3 : 1 ratio when used in the conventional way. When

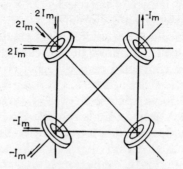

FIG. 5.11 *Three-coordinate selection array with infinite selection ratio*

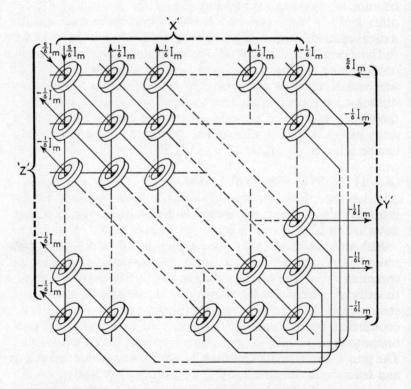

FIG. 5.12 *Three-coordinate selection array with 5:1 selection ratio*

currents of $\frac{1}{2}I_m$ flow in each of the selected X, Y and Z coordinates, the triple coincidence gives a current of $\frac{3}{2}I_m$ in the selected core and $\frac{1}{2}I_m$ in the partially selected cores. With more complex driving arrangements, in which $\frac{5}{6}I_m$ flows in the selected coordinates and $-\frac{1}{6}I_m$ in the other coordinates, the selected core is linked by a current of $\frac{5}{2}I_m$ while all the others are subjected to $\pm \frac{1}{2}I_m$, giving a 5 : 1 selection ratio. In addition to the more complicated driving circuits which are necessary, an extra set of wires threading the cores is needed and extra decoding circuits are required to select the third coordinate. To select a core in the square array of Fig. 5.12, containing 2^{2n} cores, in which extra diagonal coordinate wires have been inserted, the binary address of $2n$ digits is decoded in two groups of n digits. The two groups each select 1 out of 2^n wires for the X and Y coordinates. The address of the diagonal coordinate is found by subtracting one group of n digits from the other and taking the difference modulo 2^n. This third group of n digits is decoded to select 1 out of 2^n Z coordinate wires.

The rule which must be followed when developing threading configurations for more than three sets of wires is that only one wire should be common to any two cores. This rule makes it difficult and, in some cases, impossible, to make use of more than three windings. There is one general case, of which the 2×2 array of Fig. 5.11 is an example, where an infinite selection ratio can be achieved in theory. This is the case of a square array of p^2 cores, where p is a prime number, which can be threaded by $(p + 1)$ sets of p wires each threading p cores, to give an infinite selection ratio. This is achieved when an inhibiting current, which is in the ratio of 1 : p with the current in the $p + 1$ selected wires, flows in all the unselected wires.

Although multiple coincidence schemes have a certain theoretical interest, the practical disadvantages of increased threading complexity and of requiring a lot more drive circuits in addition to extra decoding circuits, outweigh the increase in operating speed which is possible. The maximum number of selection coordinates which could be used in practice obviously depends on the tolerances which could be maintained on the drive currents. The principle can be applied in arrays of cores used for decoding and selection as described in Chapter 9.

5.2 SYSTEMS EMPLOYING TWO CORES PER BIT

Although the read operation can be speeded up by increasing the read-current in a word-organized system, the speed with which the write operation can take place is limited by the permissible amplitude of the coincident currents which must be less than that which starts to switch unselected cores. The use of two cores to store one bit of information in a word-organized system removes

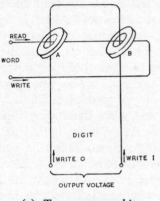

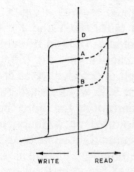

(a) *Two-cores-per-bit system*

(b) *Operating points for two-cores-per-bit system*

FIG. 5.13

the limitation on write-current and makes higher speed operation possible. In Fig. 5.13(a), if we assume that the read-current has set both cores at the remanent point D shown in Fig. 5.13(b), the application of the write-current will tend to switch both cores equally towards the other remanent point. However, a digit current in the write 0 direction as shown, when applied simultaneously with the word-write current, will aid switching in core B but oppose it in core A. Core B will therefore switch faster than core A, and, if the write-current is removed before all the flux in both cores has switched, the cores will be set at the points A and B, say, as shown. Now, when a read-current flows in the word wire, opposing e.m.f.s, corresponding to the change of flux in the cores, will be induced in the digit wire and the output voltage will be proportional to the difference in flux set into the cores. Similarly, the write-1 digit current will reverse the flux settings of the cores and thus the polarity of the output voltage.

Although the amplitude of the digit current must not be sufficiently great to disturb the cores appreciably, the amplitude of the write-current can be increased to ensure rapid switching. It can be shown that the flux change in a core depends on the time integral of the applied field in excess of the critical field which just starts switching the core, so that the duration of the current is as important as its amplitude. The flux change in the cores can therefore be limited by controlling the duration of the write-current. Partial switching of the cores reduces the drive power required. The degree to which partial switching can be applied is limited by the tolerances on the core characteristics and on the drive currents, but systems have been designed where the total flux change in both cores is less than 25 per cent of the available flux change in one core. Two-cores-per-bit systems have the added advantage over single-core systems, that a constant load, which is independent of the information content of the word, is presented to the drive currents.

Although, in principle, a slow material can be employed in two-cores-per-bit arrangements and still provide high-speed operation, the natural switching time of the core may limit the cycle time because of the following effect. During the writing operation in any core storage system, the digit current induces in the sense line a large write-breakthrough voltage due to the air coupling and the coupling via the residual permeability of the cores common to the two wires. To prevent overloading the sense-amplifier causing recovery effects (see Chapter 9), in the two-cores-per-bit arrangement of Fig. 5.14, this voltage is cancelled by reversing the direction in which the sense line threads half of the store. To keep the polarity of the output signal representing 1, the same throughout the store, the direction of the digit-write current is reversed when the selected address is in the second half of the store. This geometrical configuration does greatly reduce the write breakthrough but cancellation cannot be perfect, since the residual permeability of the cores depends on their remanent state and, hence, on the information stored in them. In the arrangement of Fig. 5.14, the pattern which makes the breakthrough a maximum is when corresponding digits in each word are the same. If there were no lag between the application of a field and the resulting flux change in the core, the write

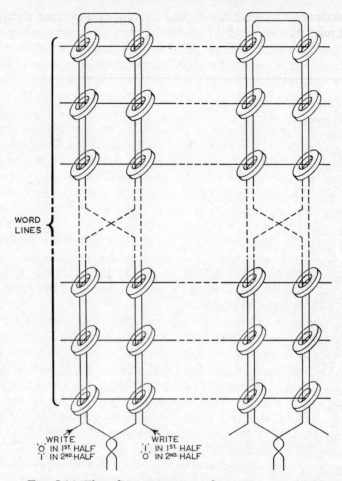

WORD
LINES

WRITE
'0' IN 1ST. HALF
'1' IN 2ND. HALF

WRITE
'1' IN 1ST. HALF
'0' IN 2ND. HALF

FIG. 5.14 *Threading arrangement for a two-cores-per-bit system*

breakthrough would only appear during the rise and decay times of the digit current. However, when the digit current is turned off, the core relaxes back to its remanent state in a time depending on the switching time of the material. The resulting voltage induced in the sense line may last for some considerable time after the digit current has decayed to zero. It is then necessary to wait until this voltage has decayed to a level low enough not to affect the discrimination before another word is read from the store. The greater the capacity of the system, the larger the amplitude of this breakthrough voltage and the longer must be the delay until the next reading operation.

5.3 MULTI-APERTURED PLATES

In an attempt to reduce the cost of manufacture and assembly of large-capacity ferrite-core stores, ferrite plates were developed with arrays of holes each of which replaces a single core.[33] For a given current linking a hole, the magnetizing field in the material is inversely proportional to the radius. The flux change around the hole due to this current is therefore confined to a certain radius within which the field is greater than the critical field required to reverse the magnetization. If this critical radius is less than half the distance between holes, there should be no interaction between adjacent holes. Although the magnetic elements no longer have to be handled individually, there are still some difficulties in threading each hole with the four conductors necessary for a three-dimensional array with two-coordinate selection and which incorporates noise cancellation.

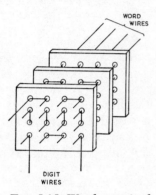

FIG. 5.15 *Word-organized ferrite plate system*

The plates lend themselves more to word selection when they can be arranged as shown in Fig. 5.15. The digit wire threading all the holes in one plate can be deposited through the holes and on alternate faces of the plate so that only the word wire has to be threaded. Because of the difficulty in obtaining the necessary high uniformity of magnetic characteristics between holes, a two-holes-per-bit system,[35] with its greater tolerance to variations in magnetic characteristics and operating conditions, and similar to the two-cores-per-bit system, may be employed.

5.4 THREE-HOLED CORES FOR HIGH-SPEED OPERATION

In an attempt to overcome the limitation in switching time of a ferrite core, because of the limited field which may be applied,

G

the three-holed ferrite element, of Fig. 5.16, was developed.[36] The direct-bias current normally saturates legs A and B in opposite directions as shown by the arrows in Fig. 5.17(a); the flux in legs C and D must then be in opposite directions and the two possible configurations are shown in Figs. 5.17(a) and (b), representing a stored 0 and 1 respectively. If the m.m.f. due to the read-current, which is applied through the centre hole via one or both of the X and Y conductors, is great enough, the flux in leg A is reversed. This results in a reversal of the flux in leg C when 0 is stored or the flux in leg D when 1 is stored. Thus, only in the case of a stored 1 is there a flux change linking the sense wire and an output signal induced. When the read-current is turned off, the flux in leg A is returned by the bias current, causing a reversal of

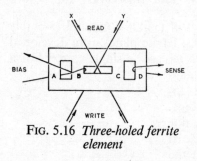

FIG. 5.16 *Three-holed ferrite element*

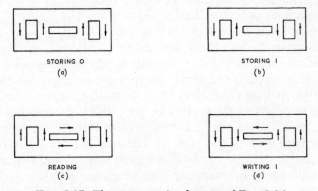

STORING O
(a)

STORING I
(b)

READING
(c)

WRITING I
(d)

FIG. 5.17 *Flux patterns in element of Fig. 5.16*

flux in the shortest magnetic path length via leg C and leaving the core in the 0 state. To write 1 into the core, a write-current of opposite polarity to the read-current is applied via the centre hole causing the flux in legs B and D to reverse. When the write-current is turned off, leg B returns to normal and the flux path is closed through leg C. Since the read- and write-currents must overcome the bias before any flux change can take place in the core, their amplitude is not limited, as it is in the conventional ferrite core. By increasing the bias current, the switching time can be considerably reduced at the expense of increased drive currents.

Alternative modes of operation of the three-holed core are possible. One method, inhibited flux operation,[38] has the advantage of requiring only one wire through each of the apertures as shown in Fig. 5.18. The word wire is threaded through the centre hole, the digit wire through one of the side holes and the digit sense wire through the other. If the m.m.f. due to the read-current in the word conductor is sufficiently great, the resulting flux pattern is as shown in

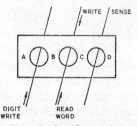

FIG. 5.18 *Alternative three-holed element*

Fig. 5.19(*a*). To write 1, the polarity of the current in the word wire is reversed and the flux is switched to the pattern shown in Fig. 5.19(*b*). To write 0 a digit current is applied simultaneously with the word current, in the direction which inhibits

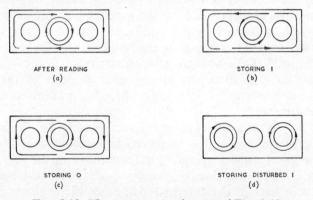

FIG. 5.19 *Flux patterns in element of Fig. 5.18*

flux from changing in leg *A* and, since the flux paths must be closed, in leg *D* as well. The resulting 0 state is shown in Fig. 5.19(*c*). If a core into which 1 has been written is subjected to a disturbing digit current when no word current is applied, the flux in legs *A* and *C* is reversed without affecting leg *D*, giving the flux pattern shown in Fig. 5.19(*d*). When a core, in either the undisturbed or disturbed 1 state, is read, the flux in leg *D* which links the sense wire is reversed and an output signal obtained. Since the flux in leg D is not reversed, no output signal is obtained when the core is storing 0.

5.5 TEMPERATURE EFFECTS

Since the Curie temperature, at which all ferromagnetism disappears, is usually between 200° and 300°C for ferrite materials, the magnetic characteristics of most ferrite cores are to some extent temperature dependent. Both the coercivity and the saturation flux density decrease with increasing temperature. Some materials have been developed[42] with improved temperature characteristics which allow two-coordinate selection over a temperature range of 100°C. The main difficulty in 2 : 1 selection systems is the variation of coercivity which results in variation of the critical current at which the core begins to switch. This variation can be allowed for, by arranging that the drive currents in the system vary with temperature in a similar way. Compensation by the addition to the current defining circuits, of a temperature-sensitive element which has the same temperature dependence and which is located in the same environment as the storage cores, can extend the operating temperature range by a considerable factor.[40] If the ambient temperature range is too great for accurate compensation, the operating temperature of the cores must be controlled at a point higher than the maximum expected temperature.[41]

Not only is the ambient temperature important, but the internal heating in the cores, due to repeated switching, may have an adverse effect on the operating characteristics of the store. The energy, which is lost due to hysteresis each time a core switches, appears as heat in the core material. Since the ferrite is a poor thermal conductor, there may be a considerable temperature rise in a core which is repeatedly switched. As the temperature increases, the area enclosed by the hysteresis loop is reduced and so the energy lost per cycle decreases. When the energy lost per cycle just compensates for the heat lost from the surface of the core, the core temperature reaches equilibrium. Since the energy lost is proportional to the volume of the core and the heat lost depends on its surface area, small cores are advantageous in high-speed systems. This self-heating effect can be reduced by ensuring that heat is efficiently transferred from the surface of the cores, either by forced air cooling or by their immersion in oil.

5.6 NON-DESTRUCTIVE READ-OUT

In some applications, the destructive nature of the reading operation is a severe limitation. Several methods, employing conventional cores or specially designed elements, have been developed to enable the information to be read non-destructively. One of the first methods suggested is the sensing of information

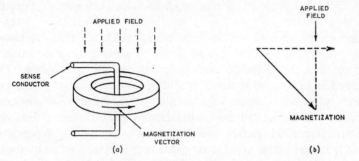

FIG. 5.20(a) *Non-destructive read-out by orthogonal field*
(b) *rotation of magnetization by orthogonal field*

stored in a core by applying a magnetic field orthogonal to the magnetization vector.[43] When an orthogonal field is applied, as illustrated in Fig. 5.20(a), the magnetization is rotated in the direction of the applied field, causing a change in the flux linked by the sense wire threading the core. The polarity of the induced e.m.f. depends on whether the magnetization is directed clockwise or anti-clockwise round the core; that is, on whether the core is storing a 1 or 0. Although the orthogonal field does reduce the remanent flux round the core, provided that the field is kept low enough, the information is not destroyed by repeated reading operations.

In the FLUXLOK[45] method of operation, all the cores in one word are placed along the axis of a solenoid, by means of which the orthogonal field is applied. Figure 5.21 illustrates two specially designed devices for non-destructive read-out (NDRO) using an orthogonal field. In Fig. 5.21(a) the BIAX element[46] consists of a

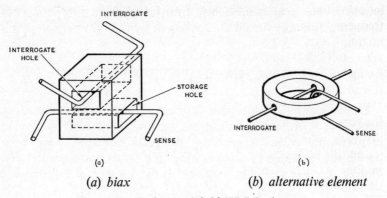

(a) biax　　　　　　　　(b) alternative element

FIG. 5.21 Orthogonal field NDRO elements

piece of ferrite with two orthogonal holes. The dimensions chosen are such that the volume of ferrite between them is common to the flux paths round both holes. If, therefore, information is stored in a conventional way round one hole, the storage hole, the field applied by means of a conductor threading the other, the interrogate hole, will be perpendicular to the stored flux. The interrogate field causes the stored flux to rotate inducing an e.m.f. in the sense conductor threading the storage hole. In the second device shown in Fig. 5.21(b), the field is applied via a conductor threading two holes in the wall of the core as shown. In this case, the interrogating field is not everywhere perpendicular to the stored flux but the net effect is similar.

It has been found[47] that the application of pulse fields, greater in amplitude than the critical field, but of less than a certain critical duration, does not cause irreversible changes in the magnetization of a core. When such a pulse is applied to a core in a direction to reverse the magnetization, large changes of flux take place, but, on the removal of the field, the core recovers to its original remanent state. This effect can be made the basis of a NDRO system[48] since the flux change which is observed depends on the remanent state of the core and therefore on the stored information. To increase the discrimination on reading, a two-cores-per-bit system, in which the read pulse duration is reduced until only reversible flux changes take place, may be employed.

One method of NDRO,[50] which appears to be suitable for large arrays, is based on the use of sine waves of high enough frequency so that only reversible flux changes take place. If a core, which is in one of its remanent states of magnetization, has two radio frequency m.m.f.s of frequencies f_1 and f_2 applied to it, frequency mixing takes place due to the non-linearity of the $\Phi-I$ characteristic. This results in the sum $(f_1 + f_2)$ and difference $(f_1 - f_2)$ frequencies appearing in an output winding threading the core. It can be shown that the phase of these frequencies differs by 180°, depending on the sign of the non-linearity, that is, whether the core is at positive or negative remanence. The output from the array, in which the selected X coordinate is driven by frequency $_1$ and the Y coordinate by f_2, is fed to a tuned amplifier as shown in Fig. 5.22. This amplifier selects the difference frequency and the stored information is sensed in a phase-detecting circuit. Since mixing takes place only in the selected core and since all

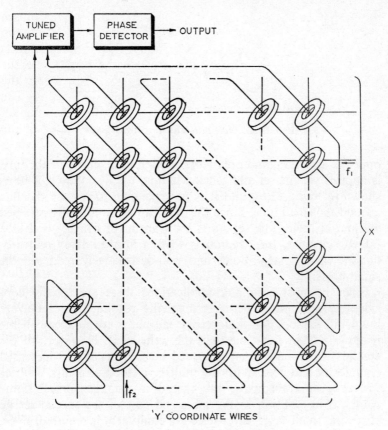

FIG. 5.22 *Radio-frequency method of non-destructive read-out*

frequencies other than the difference frequency are filtered from the output, the system is essentially noise-free.

Of the many multi-aperture elements which can be used for NDRO, the TRANSFLUXOR[51] deserves special mention as it was the first such device. Basically, the transfluxor is a core with a second small hole as shown in Fig. 5.23. When an m.m.f. large enough to saturate all the material around the large hole is applied via the block winding the flux state is as shown in Fig. 5.23(a). Because flux can only be reversed over a closed magnetic path, in this 'blocked' state it is impossible to reverse the flux round the small hole since there is always one limb saturated in the direction of the applied m.m.f., provided that this m.m.f. is not sufficient to reverse flux round the main aperture. If, now, a set m.m.f. in the

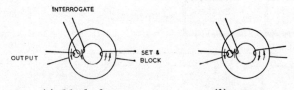

(a) blocked state (b) set state

FIG. 5.23 *Flux patterns in a transfluxor*

opposite direction, and only large enough to reverse half the flux, is applied via the set and block winding, the flux state will be as shown in Fig. 5.23(b), and it is now possible to reverse the flux around the small hole. Since this flux can be continually reversed without changing the set state, the transfluxor can be used as a NDRO element. Information is written into an array of transfluxors via the large holes and non-destructively read via the small holes.

Since in most computer applications there are usually considerably more store accesses involving reading than there are involving writing, non-destructive read-out is advantageous if the read-cycle takes less time than the write-cycle. However, all the systems which have been proposed incur a penalty in increased complexity and cost. With the multi-apertured elements, such as the biax or transfluxor, the threading arrangements become complex, in addition to the increased cost of the special ferrite structure. In all cases, extra selection equipment is required, since, in addition to the clear- (or destructive read) and write-circuits which are normally required, NDRO selection circuits are needed. This inevitably makes an NDRO system considerably more expensive than a conventional core store, so that only in special applications is it economical to provide the extra facilities. The read-out time of NDRO elements which rely on orthogonal fields (BIAX and FLUXLOK) is independent of the switching time of the ferrite material since only reversible rotational flux changes take place. In the transfluxor and allied devices the flux changes take place irreversibly by domain-wall movement and the switching time is governed by the domain-wall velocity in the material.

BIBLIOGRAPHY

GENERAL

1. Forrester, J. W. 'Digital Information Storage in Three Dimensions Using Magnetic Cores', *Jour. Applied Physics*, **22**, pp. 44–8 (1951).

2. Kincaid, M., Alden, J. M. and Hanna, R. B. 'Static Magnetic Memory for Low Cost Computers', *Electronics*, **24**, pp. 108–11 (Jan. 1951).

3. Papian, W. N. 'A Coincident Current Magnetic Memory Cell for the Storage of Digital Information', *Proc. I.R.E.*, **40**, pp. 465–78 (1952).

4. Rajchman, J. A. 'Static Magnetic Matrix Memory and Switching Circuits', *R.C.A. Review*, **13**, pp. 183–201 (1952).

5. Brown, D. R. and Albers-Schoenberg, E. 'Ferrites Speed Digital Computers', *Electronics*, **26**, pp. 146–9 (1953).

6. Menyuk, N. and Goodenough, J. C. 'Magnetic Materials for Digital Computer Components I—A Theory of Flux Reversal in Polychrystalline Ferromagnetics', *Jour. Applied Physics*, **26**, pp. 8–18 (1955).

7. Rajchman, J. A. 'A Myriabit Magnetic Core Matrix Memory', *Proc. I.R.E.*, **41**, pp. 1407–21 (1953).

8. Rajchman, J. A. 'Magnetics for Computers—A Survey of the State of the Art', *R.C.A. Rev.*, **20**, No. 1, 92–135 (March 1959).

9. Looney, D. H. 'Computer Components. Recent Advances in Magnetic Devices for Computers', *Jour. Applied Physics*, Supplement to **30**, April 1959, pp. 38S–42S.

10. Quartly, C. J. *Square-Loop Ferrite Circuitry—Storage and Logic Techniques*, Iliffe (Prentice-Hall, 1962).

11. Brown, D. A. H. 'The Behaviour of Square Loop Ferrite Cores in Circuits', *Electronic Engineering*, **31**, pp. 408–11 (1959).

12. Smit, J. and Wijn, H. P. J. *Ferrites*, Philips Technical Library (Eindhoven, Holland, 1959).

ACCESS ARRANGEMENTS

13. Mitchell, J. L. 'The TX-O, A Transistor Computer with a 256 × 256 Memory', *Proc. Eastern Joint Computer Conference*, December 1956, pp. 93–101.

14. Robinson, A. A., Newhouse, V. L., Friedman, M. J., Bindon, D. G. and Carter, I. P. V. 'A Digital Store Using a Magnetic Core Matrix', *Proc. I.E.E.*, **103**, Part B, Supplement No. 2, pp. 295–301 (1956).

15. Best, R. L. 'Memory Units in the Lincoln TX-2', *Proc. Western Joint Computer Conference*, February 1957, pp. 160–7.

16. McMahon, R. E. 'Transistorized Core Memory', *Trans. I.R.E. on Instrumentation*, **1–6**, pp. 157–60 (1957).

17. McNamara, F. 'The Noise Problem in a Coincident-current Core Memory', *Trans. I.R.E. on Instrumentation*, **1–6**, June 1957, p. 153.

18. Cooke, P. and Dillistone, D. C. 'The Measurement and Reduction of Noise in Coincident-current Core Memories', *Proc. I.E.E.*, **109**, Part B, pp. 383–9 (1962).

19. Alexander, M. A., Rosenberg, M. and Stuart Williams, R. 'Ferrite Core Memory is Fast and Reliable', *Electronics*, **29** (2), pp. 158–61 (Feb. 1956).

20. Renwick, W. 'A Magnetic-Core Matrix Store with Direct Selection Using a Magnetic Core Switch Matrix', *Proc. I.E.E.*, **104**, Part B, Supplement No. 7, pp. 436–44 (1957).

21. Foss, E. D. and Partridge, R. S. 'A 32,000 Word Magnetic Core Memory', *I.B.M. Jour. Research and Development*, **1**, No. 2, pp. 103–9 (April 1957).

22. Bray, D. and Conway, A. C. 'A Transistorized Magnetic-core Store', *Proc. I.E.E.*, **106**, Part B, Supplement No. 16, pp. 644–8 (1959).

23. Allen, C. A., Bruce, G. D. and Councill, E. D. 'A 2·18 Microsecond Megabit Core Storage Unit', *Trans. I.R.E. on Electronic Computers*, **EC–10**, pp. 233–7 (June 1961).

24. Haynes, M. K. 'Multi-Dimensional Magnetic Memory Selection Systems', *Trans. I.R.E. on Electronic Computers*, **EC–1**, pp. 25–32 (1952).

25. Minnick, R. C. and Ashenhurst, R. L. 'Multiple Coincidence Magnetic Storage Systems', *Jour. Applied Physics*, **26**, pp. 575–9 (1955).

26. Blachman, N. M. 'On the Wiring of Two-dimensional Multiple-Coincidence Magnetic Memories', *Trans. I.R.E. on Electronic Computers*, **EC–5**, pp. 19–21 (1956).

27. Schlaeppi, H. P. and Carter, I. P. V. 'Sub-microsecond Core Memories Using Multiple Coincidence', *Trans. I.R.E. on Electronic Computers*, **EC–9**, pp. 192–8 (1960).

SYSTEMS EMPLOYING TWO CORES PER BIT

28. Quartly, C. J. 'A High-speed Ferrite Storage System', *Electronic Engineering*, **31**, pp. 756–8 (1959).

29. Edwards, D. B. G., Lanigan, M. J. and Kilburn, T. 'Ferrite Core Memory Systems with Rapid Cycle-Times', *Proc. I.E.E.*, **107**, Part B, pp. 585–98 (1960).

30. Rhodes, W. H., Russell, L. A., Sakalay, F. E. and Whalen, R. M. 'A 0·7 Microsecond Ferrite Core Memory', *I.B.M. Jour. Research and Development*, **5**, pp. 174–82 (1961).

31. McMahon, R. E. 'Impulse Switching of Ferrites', *Proc. Eastern Joint Computer Conference*, Dec. 1958, pp. 31–3.

32. Tancrell, R. H. and McMahon, R. E. 'Studies in Partial Switching of Ferrite Cores', *Jour. Applied Physics*, **31**, pp. 762–71 (1960).

MULTI-APERTURED PLATES

33. Rajchman, J. A. 'Ferrite Aperture Plate for Random-access Memory', *Proc. I.R.E.*, **45**, pp. 325–34 (1957).

34. Haneman, W. J. and Lehman, J. 'Apertured Plate Memory Operation and Analysis', *I.R.E. National Convention Record*, 1958, Part 4, p. 254 (Abstract).

35. Kaufman, M. M. and Newhouse V. L. 'Operating Range of a Memory Using Two Ferrite Plate Apertures Per Bit', *Jour. Applied Physics*, **29**, pp. 487–8 (1958).

THREE-HOLED CORES FOR HIGH-SPEED OPERATION

36. Hunter, L. P. and Bauer, E. W. 'High-speed Coincident-flux Magnetic Storage Principles', *Jour. Applied Physics*, **27**, pp. 1257–61 (1956).

37. Lawrence, W. W. Jnr. 'Recent Developments in Very High-speed Magnetic Storage Techniques', *Proc. Eastern Joint Computer Conference*, Dec. 1956, pp. 101–3.

38. Baldwin, J. A. Jnr. and Rogers, J. L. 'Inhibited Flux—A New Mode of Operation of the Three-hole Memory Core', *Jour. Applied Physics*, Supplement to **30**, pp. 585–95 (1959).

39. Leaycraft, E. C. and Melan, E. H. 'Characteristics of a High-speed Multipath Core for a Coincident-Current Memory', *Trans. I.R.E. on Electronic Computers*, **EC-11**, pp. 405–9 (1962).

TEMPERATURE EFFECTS

40. Ashley, A. H. *et al.* 'Temperature Compensation for a Core Memory', *Proc. Eastern Joint Computer Conference*, Dec. 1959, pp. 200–4.

41. Straley, R., Heuer, A., Kane, B. and Tkach, G. 'Miniature Memory Planes for Extreme Environmental Conditions', *Jour. Applied Physics*, Supplement to **31**, pp. 126S–8S (1960).

42. Schwabe, E. A. and Campbell, D. A. 'Influence of Grain Size on the Square-Loop Properties of Lithium Ferrite,' *Jour. Applied Physics*, **34**, pp. 1251–3 (April, 1963, Part 2).

NON-DESTRUCTIVE READ-OUT

43. Buck, D. A. and Frank, W. I. 'Non-destructive Sensing of Magnetic Cores', *Communications and Electronics* (*Trans. A.I.E.E.*, Part 1), pp. 822–30, No. 10 (Jan. 1954).

44. Papoulis, A. 'The Non-destructive Read-out of Magnetic Cores', *Proc. I.R.E.*, **42**, pp. 1283–8 (1954).

45. Tillman, R. M. 'FLUXLOK—A Non-destructive Random-access Electrically alterable High-speed Memory Technique Using Standard Ferrite Memory Cores', *Trans. I.R.E. on Electronic Computers*, EC–9, pp. 323–8 (1960).

46. Wanlass, C. L. and Wanlass, S. D. 'BIAX High-speed Magnetic Computer Element', *I.R.E. Wescon Convention Record*, 3, 1959, Part 4, pp. 40–54.

47. Newhouse, V. L. 'The Utilization of Domain Wall Viscosity in Data Handling Devices', *Proc. I.R.E.*, **45**, No. 11, pp. 1484–92 (Nov. 1957).

48. Perry, G. H. and Widdows, S. J. 'Low-coercive Ferrite Ring Cores for Fast Non-destructively Read-store'. *Digest of Technical Papers* presented at the International Solid-State Circuits Conference, pp. 58–9, Philadelphia, February, 1960.

49. McMahon, R. E. 'A.C. and Impulse Switching Techniques for Fixed, Random-access and Analog Memory Use'. *Digest of Technical Papers* presented at the International Solid-State Circuits Conference, pp. 68–9, Philadelphia, February, 1961.

50. Widrow, B. A. 'A Radio-frequency Non-destructive Read-out for Magnetic Core Memories', *Trans. I.R.E. on Electronic Computers*, EC–3, pp. 12–15 (1954).

51. Rajchman, J. A. and Lo, A. W. 'The TRANSFLUXOR', *Proc. I.R.E.*, **44**, pp. 321–32 (1956).

52. Hammel, D. G., Morgan, W. L. and Sidnam, R. D. 'A Multi-load TRANSFLUXOR Memory', *Proc. Western Joint Computer Conference*, March, 1959, pp. 14–21.

53. Penn, T. C. and Fischer, D. G. 'A Word-oriented Transistor Driven Non-destructive Read-out Memory', *Proc. Western Joint Computer Conference*, May, 1960, pp. 83–9.

54. Vinal, A. W. 'The Development of a Multi-aperture Reluctance Switch', *Proc. Western Joint Computer Conference*, May, 1961, pp. 443–74.

CHAPTER 6

MAGNETIC-STORAGE ELEMENTS OTHER THAN CORES

In a search for higher speed operation and reduced costs, considerable research and development effort has been concentrated on the study of alternative forms of static magnetic storage. One goal of this research has been the replacement of magnetic cores which must be handled and threaded individually, by elements large numbers of which can be manufactured and assembled simultaneously. A significant increase in switching speed is made possible by the use of alternative modes of magnetization reversal, in which movement of domain walls is not required. Various geometries have been investigated in which the magnetic elements have been deposited on the surface of flat or cylindrical substrates. Techniques which have been employed for the deposition of the material include electro-plating, chemical or electro-less deposition and vacuum evaporation. Considerable difficulty has been encountered in producing a large area of material with the necessary degree of uniformity in magnetic characteristics but suitable elements are now available.

6.1 THIN MAGNETIC FILMS

In 1955, Blois showed[1] that it was possible to produce magnetic films between 1000 and 10000 Å thick which exhibited a rectangular hysteresis loop and which might conceivably replace ferrite cores in a coincident-current operated store. While the reversal of magnetization takes place by domain-wall motion in a bulk ferromagnetic material, it has been shown that the reversal in a thin film may take place by a coherent rotation of the direction of magnetization. Since the factors limiting the velocity of domain-wall movement do not apply to coherent rotation, much higher operating speeds are possible. The magnetic films which have been produced so far are not suitable for coincident-current operation, since this requires very close tolerances on the coercivity of the material. The systems which are under development are all word-organized and do not rely on high uniformity of coercive force.

In a magnetic film having *uni-axial anisotropy*, the direction of magnetization is constrained to lie along the preferred or easy direction in the absence of an applied magnetic field, as shown in Fig. 6.1(*a*). The two possible directions, which are separated by 180°, of the magnetization vector can be taken to represent the binary digits 0 and 1. The hysteresis loops of such a film are shown in Fig. 6.2. In the easy direction a conventional rectangular loop is obtained while in the hard direction, perpendicular to the easy direction, the characteristic is linear with no hysteresis. H_c is the coercivity in the easy direction and H_k is the field required to align the magnetization in the hard direction. When a magnetic field is applied at an angle to the easy direction, the resulting torque causes the magnetization to rotate towards the direction of the applied field. An opposing torque occurs because of the anisotropy of the film and the vector takes up an equilibrium position where the opposing torques are equal. When the field is removed, the magnetization returns to the easy direction.

If a sufficiently large word field is applied in the hard direction, the magnetization rotates into the direction of the applied field as shown in Fig. 6.1(*b*). To write information into the element, the magnetization must be forced to return to the 1 or 0 direction by the application of a digit field, which is less than H_c and there-fore insufficient to reverse the magnetization, parallel to the easy direction, as shown in Fig. 6.1(*c*). When the word field is removed, the magnetization becomes aligned with the applied digit field, Fig. 6.1(*d*), and remains in that equilibrium position when the digit field is removed, Fig. 6.1(*e*). Alternative modes of operation are possible which remove the need for a bi-directional digit field. For example, in Fig. 6.3, the word field is applied at a small angle to the hard direction so that, when it is removed, the magnetization always returns to the 0 direction. To write 1 in this case, a digit field is applied at right angles to the word field, causing the magnetization to return to the 1 direction when the

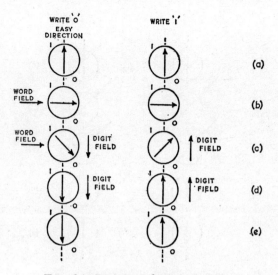

FIG. 6.1 *Rotation of magnetization in uni-axial anisotropic film*

(a) *no applied field*
(b) *word field applied*
(c) *word and digit fields applied*
(d) *digit field applied*
(e) *field removed*

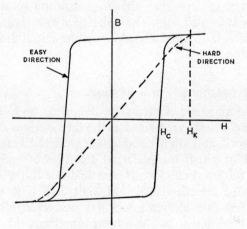

FIG. 6.2 *Hysteresis loops of film with uni-axial anisotropy*

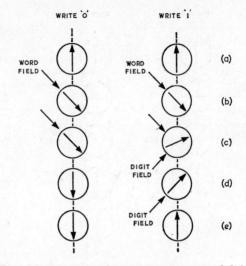

FIG. 6.3 *Rotation of magnetization—word field applied at angle to easy direction*

word and digit fields are removed. Similar operation can be achieved by applying a constant biasing field in the 0 direction and overcoming this by a digit field when writing 1. The information is read by detecting the e.m.f. induced in a sense conductor by the change of flux when the magnetization rotates under the influence of the word field. The polarity of this signal depends on the sense of rotation and therefore on the initial direction of the magnetization.

6.1.1 FLAT MAGNETIC FILM SYSTEMS

When the magnetic elements are deposited on a flat substrate, the storage elements are placed at the intersections formed by an array of word and digit conductors arranged orthogonally, as shown in Fig. 6.4. If the preferred direction of magnetization is parallel to the word conductors, the field due to the word current is in the hard direction while the digit field is in the preferred direction. Separate elements, circular or rectangular in shape,[5] have been used and it has also been found possible to employ a continuous sheet of magnetic film.[6] In the continuous film only the areas under the intersections act as storage elements.

The magnetic material, which is usually based on an alloy

containing 80 per cent nickel and 20 per cent iron, or permalloy, can be deposited by any of the methods mentioned above but the most widely used method is vacuum evaporation. Glass provides the necessary flat smooth surface on to which the film may be deposited, although a polished metallic substrate has certain advantages. Uni-axial anisotropy is induced in the film by carrying out the deposition in the presence of a uniform magnetic field with which the preferred direction of magnetization becomes aligned. Electro-deposition,[11] from a mixed bath containing the constituents of the required alloy in solution, on to a conducting substrate, is an alternative method of preparing the magnetic films. Films, based on a nickel-cobalt alloy, can also be deposited on a suitable substrate by the chemical reduction of nickel and cobalt compounds.[12] A fourth method of deposition which has been reported[13] is carried out by ionic sputtering on to the substrate, from a cathode made of the required composition in an atmosphere of argon at reduced pressure. Where separate elements are required, these can be fabricated either by deposition through a mask or by photo-etching techniques.

The magnetic film must be thin enough to ensure that only single domains can exist through its thickness. The other dimensions of the element are determined by self-demagnetizing effects and must be large enough, in relation to the thickness, to avoid deterioration of the rectangular hysteresis loop in the easy direction, since the stored information would then be disturbed by the

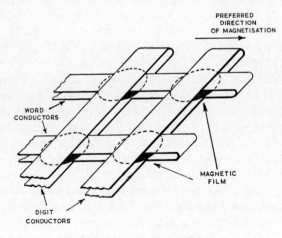

FIG. 6.4 *Flat magnetic film array*

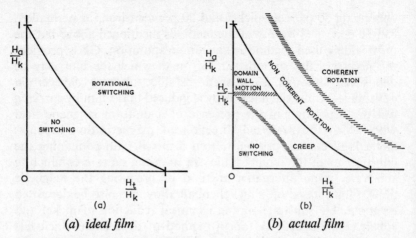

(a) ideal film   (b) actual film

FIG. 6.5 *Switching threshold characteristic for thin magnetic film*

digit field. For the same reason, the coercive force, H_c, must be kept reasonably constant and must not be much lower than the anisotropy field, H_k. It has been found that the coercivity depends on film thickness but does not vary much in the region of 1000 Å. By careful substrate preparation and control of the film thickness, reproducibility of the coercive force to within 10 per cent can be achieved. To reduce the effect of mechanical strains on the magnetic properties of the film, a low value of magnetostrictive coefficient is advantageous, hence the concentration on alloys based on 80–20 nickel iron, which has zero magnetostriction.

Because of imperfections in the magnetic properties of the material, the simple theoretical model of the switching process is not borne out in practice. The switching threshold characteristic for the simple model is plotted in Fig. 6.5(a) as a function of the applied field parallel to the easy axis, H_a, and the applied transverse field in the hard direction, H_t. A typical switching threshold characteristic is shown in Fig. 6.5(b), illustrating the more complex behaviour of the film. With little or no transverse field applied and the parallel field only slightly greater than the coercivity, H_c, the reversal of magnetization takes place slowly by the movement of domain walls. As the threshold for rotational switching is exceeded, the film commences to switch by non-coherent rotation, in which part of the magnetization reverses by rotation and the remainder by some slower mechanism. As the applied resultant field is increased, the film switches completely by a coherent rotation of the magnetization. Below the theoretical threshold where switching should cease, there is the 'creep' region in which irreversible changes take place after repeated applications of the field. The boundaries between the various modes of switching are not well defined and vary with material properties and experimental conditions. For high-speed switching, operation in the coherent rotation mode is desirable.

Although it is possible that the thin magnetic film store may ultimately have the advantage of low manufacturing costs, there are some severe problems in its practical application to high-speed, large-capacity systems. Because of the very small element cross-section, the output signal is typically only a few millivolts. The increased sensitivity required in the read amplifier makes it very difficult to avoid a long recovery time due to overloading of the amplifier by the signals induced on the sense conductor during the write operation. The low signal level also demands that capacitive and inductive pickup from the drive conductors and interference from external sources should be kept to a very low level. Because of the self- and cross-demagnetization of elements with an open flux path, the minimum size of element appears to be about one half-millimetre, with the same spacing between elements, so that the packing density is not likely to exceed 10 bits per cm. The need for word-organized systems makes the access circuits for large capacities more expensive than for cores, with which two-coordinate selection can be employed.

Arrays of storage elements are now available and several complete systems are in an advanced state of development in various laboratories. The capacities and cycle times which it is hoped to achieve with these developments range from 128 to 4096 words and 0·1 to 1 microsecond. A small store of 128 words with a cycle time of 0·6 microseconds is the first system to be incorporated in a commercially available computer, the UNIVAC, 1107.

6.1.2 CYLINDRICAL MAGNETIC FILMS

Other arrangements have been described in which the thin magnetic film is deposited on a cylindrical substrate, with the preferred direction of magnetization either circumferential[17] or axial.[16] In the first case, nickel-iron is deposited on the surface of a glass tube in the presence of a circumferential field due to a

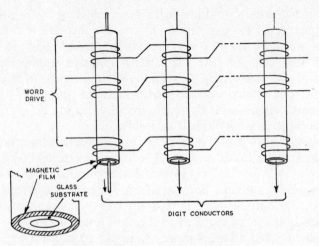

FIG. 6.6 *Cylindrical magnetic film array*

current flowing in a conductor passing through the tube. The store is arranged as shown in Fig. 6.6. The word field is applied parallel to the axis of the tube via a solenoidal winding while the digit field is applied circumferentially by means of a conductor threading the tube. Writing into an element requires simultaneous application of word and digit fields, as in the orthogonal coincident-field operation of a flat magnetic film. The word drive aligns the magnetization in the hard direction along the rod, while the polarity of the digit field determines the sense in which the magnetization returns to the easy direction round the rod when the word field is removed. The polarity of the output voltage induced in the digit conductor when the word field is applied depends on the sense of the magnetization and hence on the stored information. The cylindrical element of this type has the advantage of being a closed magnetic circuit with no demagnetizing effects, so that the size of the elements could, in theory, be reduced and the packing density increased.

In the second type of element, where the preferred direction of magnetization is aligned along the length of the cylinder, the windings are arranged as shown in Fig. 6.7. Here both word and digit fields are applied by means of solenoidal windings and the element does not rely on orthogonal fields. The operation is similar to a magnetic-core system since it relies on current coincidence in two or three of the windings. If the coercivity of the

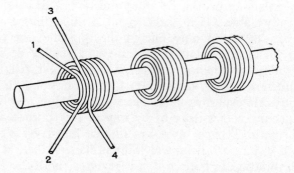

FIG. 6.7 *Alternative cylindrical film arrangement*

magnetic material is sufficiently uniform, two-coordinate read selection can be employed using four windings, one for X and the second for Y drive, the third for sense and the fourth for inhibit. The advantages which are claimed for this 'rod' element include reduced volume of magnetic material and higher speed operation. The higher operating speed is obtained by using a material with a high coercive force, some 14 oersteds compared with 1 or 2 oersteds for ferrite cores.

6.1.3 MULTI-LAYER MAGNETIC FILM ELEMENTS

The advantages of very wide operating current tolerances and less stringent demands on the magnetic properties of the film

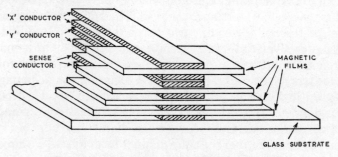

FIG. 6.8 *Multi-layer magnetic film element*

are claimed[20] for the structure with four magnetic layers shown in Fig. 6.8, which shows a section through the element. The magnetic planes are arranged so that the magnetostatic energy of the system is a minimum when any two films are magnetized in one direction

and the remaining two in the other direction. This configuration
is inherently stable. On the other hand, if three films are aligned
in one direction and only one in the opposite direction, the
resulting high-energy state is unstable and quickly decays to a
stable equilibrium condition. Since, as shown in Fig. 6.8, the films
are of different widths, this change from an unstable to a stable
equilibrium state always takes place via the film involving the
least expenditure of energy or by way of the shortest available
magnetic path. Typical operation of this four-layer element is
illustrated in Fig. 6.9, from which it will be seen that, before the
magnetization in the bottom film is reversed, both the X and Y
drive current must be applied. When the drive currents are
removed, the configuration of 6.9(d) remains stable. An output

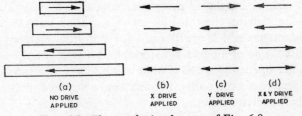

| (a) | (b) | (c) | (d) |
| NO DRIVE APPLIED | X DRIVE APPLIED | Y DRIVE APPLIED | X & Y DRIVE APPLIED |

FIG. 6.9 *Flux paths in element of Fig. 6.8*

voltage is induced in the sense conductor only when the bottom
film reverses. The structure of Fig. 6.8 is built up by successive
evaporations of aluminium conductors, silicon oxide insulators
and magnetic films of 80 per cent nickel and 20 per cent iron.

In the 'Bicore' element,[22] two magnetic films are used to give
non-destructive read-out. One film, the storage film, is a high-
coercivity nickel-cobalt alloy, while the other, the read-out film,
is a low-coercivity nickel-iron alloy. A section through an element
is shown in Fig. 6.10. The elements, which are circular in shape
with a diameter of 0·05 in., are deposited by successive evaporations
on a glass substrate and the word and digit conductors are fabricated by conventional photo-etching techniques. These conductors, in general, run at right angles to each other across the
array but in the vicinity of each element they run parallel to each
other and perpendicular to the easy direction of magnetization
in the films. The patterns of magnetization in the films for a
stored 1 and 0 are shown in Fig. 6.11. The external demagnetizing
field of the high-coercivity storage film is sufficient to saturate

the read-out film in the direction which closes the flux path between the films. If a read field, which does not exceed the coercive force of the storage film, but is large enough to overcome the external demagnetizing field, is applied in the direction shown, via the word conductor, the read-out film will be switched when 1 is stored in the element. An e.m.f. is induced in the digit conductor, therefore, only when the element is storing 1. When the field is removed,

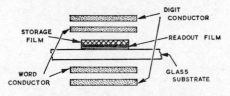

FIG. 6.10 *'Bicore' film element*

the external field of the storage film restores the read-out film to its original state. Coincident-current writing into the storage film is employed; the word write-current is augmented when writing 1 or inhibited when writing 0 by a positive or negative current in

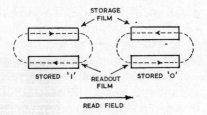

FIG. 6.11 *Pattern of magnetization in 'bicore' element*

the digit conductor. The $3:1$ selection ratio thus achieved reduces the required tolerance on the coercivity of the magnetic material.

6.2 THE TWISTOR

Another magnetic element, the Twistor, is so named because it makes use of the effect of torsion on a rod of magnetic material. When a rod of magnetic material is held under torsion, as shown in Fig. 6.12, the resulting stress in the rod has a component of maximum compression at an angle of 45° with respect to the axis of the rod and a component of maximum tension at the same angle but in the opposite screw sense. If the magnetic material is strain sensitive and has a negative magnetostrictive coefficient, the preferred direction of magnetization will follow the direction of greatest compression. If the magnetostrictive coefficient is positive, the preferred direction will be along the direction of greatest tension. The magnetization is then constrained to follow

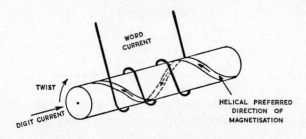

FIG. 6.12 *'Twistor' magnetic element*

a helical path as shown in Fig. 6.12. To read the information stored in a cell, a field, great enough to reverse the magnetization, is applied parallel to the axis of the rod, by means of a word current in the solenoid. If the magnetization was previously in the direction of the applied field, a small output voltage is observed between the ends of the rod. On the other hand, if the magnetization is reversed by the read-current, corresponding to a stored 1, a relatively large e.m.f. is induced between the ends of the rod by the circumferential component of the flux change. To write into the cell, a current of opposite polarity to the read-current is turned on in the solenoid and simultaneously a digit current is applied to the rod itself. Since neither of these currents alone is of sufficient amplitude to reverse the magnetization, only the cells in which the currents are coincident are switched to the 1 state.

Another mode of operation, suitable for three-dimensional arrays with coincident-current selection, is possible. In this arrangement, the X and Y coordinate and inhibit currents are applied via three solenoids, while the information is sensed across the rod itself.

The rod may be either a solid magnetic wire with torsion

applied, or a conducting non-magnetic wire on to which the magnetic material, in the form of a thin foil, is helically wrapped,[25] when no torsion need be applied. The required magnetic characteristics can also be produced by electro-deposition of the magnetic material on to a copper wire, in the presence of circumferential and axial magnetic fields which give the necessary helical preferred direction.[26] Many bits of information can be stored on one wire without mutual interference. The maximum permissible packing density is a function of the magnetic properties of the wire and its diameter; with a 0·003 in. diameter nickel wire, for example, 10 bits per inch may be stored. Since the solenoids may be replaced by single conductors, it is possible that an array, consisting of a set of parallel magnetic wires with a set of conducting wires at right angles, might be fabricated by weaving techniques.

6.3 OTHER PROPOSED MAGNETIC ELEMENTS

Another development which employs weaving techniques has been described. Bare and insulated copper wires are woven into a screen which is then plated with magnetic material to form

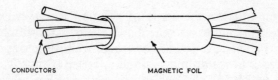

CONDUCTORS   MAGNETIC FOIL

FIG. 6.13 *Wrapped foil magnetic element*

closed magnetic circuits.[27] The insulated wires thread the magnetic elements to form an array of storage elements similar to a ferrite-core plane. If the problems in producing elements with the required uniformity of magnetic properties can be solved, this woven screen store would appear to offer the possibility of low manufacturing cost.

Threading of the magnetic elements is also avoided in the element shown in Fig. 6.13 in which the magnetic material is wrapped round a preformed bundle of conductors.[28] The magnetic material, an alloy of 79 per cent nickel, 4 per cent molybdenum and 17 per cent iron, is in the form of a thin foil rolled down to a thickness of 0·125 thousandths of an inch. In principle, the wires in an array could be assembled in the required configuration before the foil is wrapped round the appropriate intersections.

6.4 DOMAIN-WALL STORAGE

A recent proposal[29] has suggested the use of the two possible senses of rotation of the magnetization as it changes from one direction to the opposite through a domain wall, as a storage mechanism. Since the energy associated with the wall does not

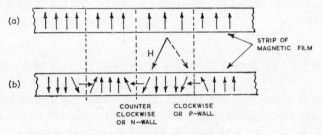

FIG. 6.14 *Domain-wall storage*

depend on whether the sense of rotation is clockwise or anti-clockwise, both states are stable and can be used to represent the two binary digits. A method, by which walls of known sense can be injected into a thin magnetic film, is shown in Fig. 6.14. If a field, H, which is sufficient to reverse a section of the film, is applied in the direction shown, two walls of opposite sense are formed as shown in Fig. 6.14(*b*). By applying the field in the direction shown dotted, the sense of the two walls is reversed, that is the *N*-wall becomes a *P*-wall and vice-versa.

This mechanism would lend itself to a serial-access storage system and Fig. 6.15 illustrates how a number of walls, representing stored information, could be shifted along a strip of magnetic film. The domains are alternately magnetized in opposite directions and the information is stored in the sense of rotation of the magnetization vector between domains. The pattern P N P P N is shown for example in Fig. 6.15(*a*). It would be possible to shift the information by applying the pattern of current pulses shown

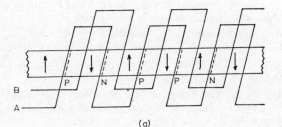

(a)

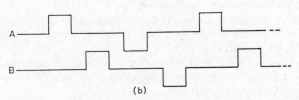

(b)

FIG. 6.15 *Shifting of domain walls along a magnetic film*
(a) conductor pattern required
(b) current waveforms required

in Fig. 6.15(*b*) to the conductors. The magnetic field due to a pulse of current in conductor *A* will move the walls until they lie under conductor *B*. When a current is applied to *B*, the walls again move to the right until they lie under conductor *A* once more. Since the magnetization in the domains is alternately in opposite directions, the current pulses applied to the conductors must alternate in polarity as shown.

BIBLIOGRAPHY

1. Blois, M. S. 'Preparation of Thin Magnetic Films and Their Properties', *Jour. Applied Physics*, **26**, pp. 975–80 (1955).

2. Conger, R. L. 'Magnetization Reversal in Thin Films', *Phys. Rev.*, **98**, pp. 1752–4 (1955).

3. Smith, D. O. 'Magnetization Reversal in Thin Films', *Phys. Rev.*, **104**, pp. 1280–1 (Dec. 1, 1956).

4. Pohm, A. V. and Rubens, S. V. 'A Compact Coincident-current Memory', *Proc. Eastern Joint Computer Conference*, Dec. 1956, pp. 120–3.

FLAT FILMS

5. Raffel, J. I., Crowther, T. S., Anderson, A. H. and Herndon, T. O. 'Magnetic Film Memory Design', *Proc. I.R.E.*, **49**, pp. 155–64 (1961).

6. Bradley, E. M. 'A Computer Storage Matrix Using Ferromagnetic Thin Films', *Jour. Brit. I.R.E.*, **20**, pp. 765–84 (1960).

7. Pohm, A. V. and Mitchell, E. N. 'Magnetic Film Memories—A Survey', *Trans. I.R.E. on Electronic Computers*, **EC–9**, pp. 308–14 (1960).

8. Bittman, E. E. 'Thin Film Memories', *Trans. I.R.E. on Electronic Computers*, **EC–8**, No. 2, pp. 92–7 (June 1, 1959).

9. Proebster, W. E. 'The Design of a High-speed Thin Magnetic Film Memory', *Digest of Technical Papers*, presented at Solid-State Circuits Conference in Philadelphia, Feb. 1962, pp. 38–9.

10. Kell, R. C. 'Magnetic Films for Storage of Information', *Brit. Communications and Electronics*, **9**, pp. 494–7 (1962).

11. Wolf, I. W. and Crowther, T. S. 'Reproducibility of Electro-deposited Thin Film Memory Arrays', *Proc. Electronic Components Conference*, 1960, pp. 116–21.

12. Heritage, R. J. and Walker, Mrs. M. T. 'Chemically Deposited Nickel-Cobalt Layers as High Speed Storage Elements', *Jour. of Electronics and Control*, **7**, pp. 542–52 (1959).

13. Francombe, M. H. and Noreika, A. J. 'Some Properties of Uniaxial Permalloy Films Prepared by Cathodic Sputtering', *Jour. Applied Physics*, Supplement to **32** (3), pp. 97S–8S (1961).

14. Dietrich, W., Proebster, W. E. and Wolf, P. 'Nano-second Switching in Thin Magnetic Films', *I.B.M. Jour. Research and Development*, **4**, pp. 189–96 (1960).

15. Williams, M. 'Magnetic Film Storage Elements: A Novel Analysis of Known Systems Which Leads to New Systems Tolerating Misoriented Films', *Proc. I.E.E.*, **109**, Part B, Supplement No. 21, pp. 186–94 (1962).

CYLINDRICAL FILMS

16. Meier, D. A. 'Millimicrosecond Magnetic Switching and Storage Element', *Jour. Applied Physics*, Supplement to **20** (4), pp. 45S–46S (1959).

17. Hoffman, G. R., Turner, J. A. and Kilburn, T. 'High-speed Digital Storage Using Cylindrical Magnetic Films', *Jour. Brit. I.R.E.*, **20**, pp. 31–6 (1960).

18. Meir, D. A. 'Magnetic-film Rods Provide High-speed Memory', *Electronics*, **35** (5), pp. 50–2 (Feb. 2, 1962).

19. Maclachlan, D. F. A. 'A Woven Memory Matrix with Cylindrical Electroplated Elements', *Brit. Communications and Electronics*, **9**, pp. 602–4 (Aug. 1962).

MULTI-LAYER FILMS

20. Broadbent, K. D. 'A Vacuum Evaporated Random Access Memory', *Proc. I.R.E.*, **48**, pp. 1728–31 (1960).

21. Oakland, L. J. and Rossing, T. D. 'Coincident-current Non-destructive Read-out from Thin Magnetic Films', *Jour. Applied Physics*, Supplement to **30**, pp. 54S–5S (1959).

22. Petschauer, R. J. and Turquist, R. D. 'A Non-destructive Read-out Film Memory', *Proc. Western Joint Computer Conference*, May, 1961, pp. 411–25.

23. Bestler, G. and Wicks, A. A. 'Thin-film Memory Elements for Computers', *Electronics*, **35**, p. 86 (1962).

TWISTOR

24. Bobeck, A. H. 'A New Storage Element Suitable for Large-sized Memory Arrays—The Twistor', *Bell System Technical Jour.*, **30**, pp. 1319–40 (1957).

25. Fisher, R. F. and Mallery, P. 'Counter Wrapped Twistor', *Proc. Electronic Components Conference*, Washington D.C., May, 1960, pp. 129–33.

26. Schwartz, S. J. and Sallo, J. S. 'Electro-deposited Twistor and Bit Wire Components', *Trans. I.R.E. on Electronic Computers*, **EC–8**, pp. 465–9 (1959).

OTHER MAGNETIC ELEMENTS

27. Howard, R. A., Wells, P. E., Cann, L. and Davis, J. S. 'Investigation of Woven Screen Memory Techniques', *Large Capacity Memory Techniques for Computing Systems*. Edited by M. C. Yovits, Macmillan and Co. (New York, 1962), pp. 361–72.

28. Tracy, R. A. 'Megabit Memory', *Proc. Eastern Joint Computer Conference*, Dec. 1956, pp. 104–6.

DOMAIN-WALL STORAGE

29. Smith, D. O. 'Proposal for Magnetic Domain-wall Storage and Logic', *Trans. I.R.E. on Electronic Computers*, **EC–10**, pp. 709–11 (1961).

CHAPTER 7

NON-MAGNETIC RANDOM-ACCESS STORAGE

ALTHOUGH the bulk of high-speed random-access stores now make use of ferrite cores, various non-magnetic elements have been developed which have advantages in certain applications. The first truly random-access store was the electrostatic storage tube, which was described in Chapter 3, and this is still occasionally employed in applications where its characteristics prove especially advantageous. The store in the ENIAC consisted of bi-stable trigger circuits or flip-flops which are now widely used in the arithmetic and control-register circuits of most digital computers. The flip-flop is an example of the class of negative-resistance devices, several of which have been employed or suggested for storage. A recent promising development in this field of negative-resistance elements is the tunnel diode which has been incorporated in several stores now in operation. Since 1956, when the first paper on the 'cryotron' was published, intensive research has been conducted into methods of utilizing the phenomenon of super-conductivity for the storage of digital information. The stimulus behind this 'cryo-electric' work is the hope of producing very large-capacity random-access stores at low cost.

7.1 NEGATIVE-RESISTANCE STORAGE ELEMENTS

Any device which has a voltage/current characteristic with a negative-resistance region, can be suitably biased to give two stable operating points which may be taken to represent the binary digits 0 and 1. Two types of negative resistance are possible, the voltage-controlled characteristic of Fig. 7.1(*a*) and the current-controlled characteristic of Fig. 7.1(*b*). In the first case, the current through the device is a single-valued function of the voltage applied to it, while the voltage is not uniquely determined by the current; in the second case the voltage is a single-valued function of the current which is, however, not uniquely determined by the voltage. By choosing a suitable bias voltage E, and a suitable load resistance R, the load line can be made to intersect the characteristic at three points as shown in Fig. 7.1. Two of these points, A and B, correspond to stable equilibrium states; the third point, C, corresponds to a condition of unstable equilibrium since any deviation from equilibrium causes the operating

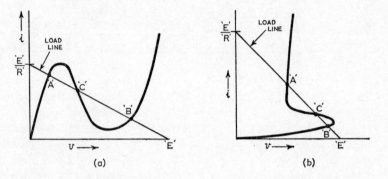

(a) voltage controlled   (b) current controlled

FIG. 7.1 *Negative resistance characteristics*

point to move further away until it reaches one of the stable positions. A necessary condition for two stable equilibrium states in the voltage-controlled case is that the load resistance R must be greater than the slope of the characteristic in the negative-resistance region, while in the current-controlled case, R must be less than the slope. Stores have been built with various negative-resistance elements, including the gas-filled diode or voltage stabilizer tube, the conventional Eccles-Jordan bi-stable or flip-flop circuit, using vacuum tubes or transistors and the tunnel or Esaki diode. The 'Cryosar', which has a negative resistance at temperatures near to absolute zero, has also been suggested as a suitable element for digital storage.

7.1.1 GAS TUBES

One of the first random-access stores to be described[1] employed glow discharge tubes which consist of two electrodes mounted in an atmosphere of an inert gas at reduced pressure. The resistance of such a device is very high until the striking voltage is reached, when the gas becomes ionized and the resistance of the tube drops to a very low value. Since the voltage required to maintain the discharge is usually considerably lower than the striking voltage, the characteristic is similar to Fig. 7.1(*b*). In the array of Fig. 7.2,

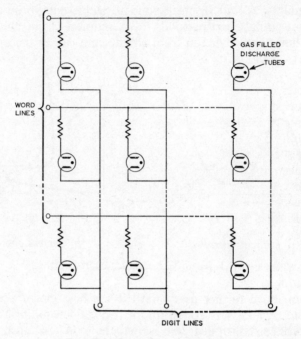

FIG. 7.2 *Gas-tube storage array*

it is possible to strike one tube only, by the simultaneous application of voltage pulses to the word and digit lines. If the bias voltage and load resistance are suitably chosen, the voltages applied to the selected row and column only change the state of the tube common to both. Since the impedance between the selected word line and the digit lines is either very high (stored 0) or very low (stored 1), the information can be read by detecting the current change in the digit lines when the word voltage is varied on the selected word.

Although ionization of the gas takes place rapidly, times in the order of 1 millisecond are required for the tube to return to its high resistance state when the voltage is reduced below the maintaining voltage. Consequently the writing speed is low. Due to difficulties in maintaining the required uniformity of the tube characteristics, this type of store has never been of much practical importance. Special gas tubes, in which the discharge takes place from the cathode to one of ten anodes, have been widely used for decimal counting and storage operations where high speed is not required.[3]

7.1.2 BI-STABLE CIRCUITS

The conventional flip-flop or Eccles-Jordan bi-stable[4] circuit of Fig. 7.3(a) has two stable states in which one transistor is conducting and the other is cut-off. The negative-resistance characteristic of the element is obtained by the positive feedback due to the circuit configuration. If the current flowing into one collector with no load resistor connected, is measured as a function of the voltage applied to the collector, a characteristic similar to Fig. 7.1(a) is obtained. The flip-flop requires extra logic circuits for selection and a typical arrangement to store a single binary digit is shown in Fig. 7.3(b), with its input (or write) and output (or read) gates.

Although elements of the type shown in Fig. 7.3(b) can be connected to form a complete storage system, the complexity and cost rule out very large capacities. Flip-flops are usually employed in the arithmetic and control registers of a computer, or in buffer store applications, where high-speed access is essential and only a few words of storage are required. Since the flip-flop is constructed of components and circuit techniques similar to the remainder of the logic circuits,

I

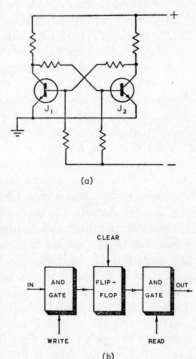

FIG. 7.3 (a) *Bi-stable circuit element* (b) *One-bit storage element*

the input and output signal levels are compatible and no extra buffer amplifiers are necessary.

7.1.3 TUNNEL DIODES

In the tunnel diode, discovered by Esaki in 1958,[5] the negative resistance is caused by the tunnelling of electrons through a narrow *PN* junction between very highly doped regions in a semiconductor. The current/voltage characteristic obtained is of the form shown in Fig. 7.1(*a*). As the voltage across the diode is increased from zero, the tunnelling current first increases to reach a peak value (at about 50 millivolts for germanium) and then decreases as the voltage increases to give a negative-resistance region. At higher voltages the current follows the normal forward characteristic of a semiconductor diode; the point at which the current starts to increase again is determined by the energy gap of the material and is about 400 millivolts for germanium. The peak current of the diode depends on the junction area and may range from 1 milliampere upwards. Since the time taken to change from one state to the other is typically 1 nanosecond (10^{-9} second), an array of suitably biased tunnel diodes provides a means of high-speed storage.

At least one other component, a biasing resistor to maintain the correct operating conditions, is required. It is possible to switch one tunnel diode in an array similar to the gas-tube array of Fig. 7.2, by applying coincident voltage pulses to the selected word and digit lines. The information is read by sensing the change of current in the digit line when the tunnel diode is switched by the word drive. The detection of this current change, in the presence of the direct current equal to the sum of the bias currents from all the diodes connected to the digit line, requires complex cancellation circuits and accurate balancing of the digit lines.[6] To facilitate reading and writing, other components are added which effectively provide a storage element with more than the two terminals of the diode itself. One of the first arrangements suggested[7] is shown in Fig. 7.4(*a*), where it will be seen that two resistors, one capacitor and one transformer have been added to the tunnel diode. This element is suitable for two-coordinate selection with the *X* and *Y* selection voltages applied to the terminals as shown and the digit inhibit voltage applied to the *Z* terminal. Since the drive is linearly coupled to the sense output, however, the noise signals from half-selected elements severely limit the size of the array which can be employed.

The element shown in Fig. 7.4(*b*) has become a preferred configuration and variants have been used in several stores which are now in operation.[10, 11] By adding the rectifier diode, the discrimination is increased and the arrangement of the store, which is shown in Fig. 7.5, is simplified. Typical operating waveforms are illustrated in Fig. 7.6. To read the information a negative voltage pulse is applied to word line *A*; this causes the rectifier diode to become forward biased in the elements where the tunnel diode is in the low voltage, or 1, state and a current flows in the digit line. The voltage drop across those tunnel diodes

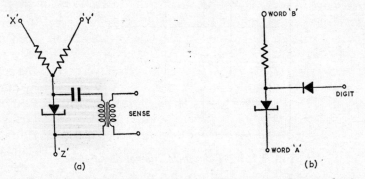

FIG. 7.4(*a*) *Tunnel-diode storage element for two-coordinate selection*
  (*b*) *Tunnel-diode storage element for word-organized system*

in the high voltage state prevents the rectifier diodes conducting in the case of a stored 0. When writing, the tunnel diode is returned to its low voltage state by the application of a negative pulse to word line *B*, while the digit line is driven negative to write 1, or left at its normal potential to write 0. Thus, when word line *B* returns to the normal bias level, the tunnel diodes are left in the required equilibrium condition. In the above mode of operation, reading destroys the stored information if the impedance of the digit line is low. Non-destructive sensing can be carried out by restricting the current which flows in the digit line, to less than the difference between the tunnel-diode peak current and the bias current.[10] The tolerances in non-destructive operation are improved if the bias current is maintained constant during reading by moving both word lines *A* and *B* through equal voltage excursions. The discrimination between 1 and 0 is the voltage difference between the low and high states of the tunnel diode.

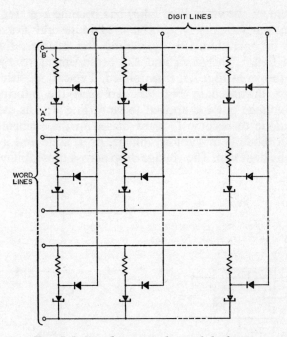

FIG. 7.5 *Word-organized tunnel-diode store*

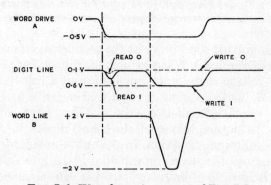

FIG. 7.6 *Waveforms in system of Fig. 7.5*

Since the tunnel-diode storage element requires at least one biasing resistor and usually more components in addition to the diode itself, the cost per bit is comparatively high. In addition, the increased number of components and connections per element decreases the packing density and increases the risk of failure. In addition to the advantage of high operating speed, the tunnel-diode store requires only moderate currents and low voltages from the drive circuits compared with magnetic elements. Conventional assembly techniques are convenient for low-capacity tunnel-diode stores but larger systems will require radical changes to improve packing density and minimize transmission delays if high-speed operation is required. The construction of a store from integral units consisting of arrays of elements, each of which includes all the necessary components, would have obvious advantages and the application of new semiconductor manufacturing processes may make this possible.

7.1.4 THE CRYOSAR

The resistance of a bar of germanium, which is cooled to a temperature some degrees above absolute zero, is voltage dependent. Since nearly all the carriers are attached to impurity-centres at these low temperatures, the resistance is extremely high until the applied electric field reaches a critical value when the free carriers gain enough energy to ionize the impurity-centres on impact. When this occurs, the resistance becomes very low and the voltage remains substantially constant while the current increases by several orders of magnitude. If the germanium is compensated, that is, contains both N and P type impurities, it has been found that there is a region of negative resistance between the high and low resistance states giving a voltage-current characteristic similar to Fig. 7.1(b). The cryosar can therefore be used as a storage element and, since only ohmic contacts are required to the germanium, elements can be fabricated as arrays on a single semiconductor wafer.[12] A set of parallel conductors is deposited on one side of the wafer and a perpendicular set on the other, giving the arrangement shown in Fig. 7.7. A compound structure can be made which also includes the necessary load resistance for bi-stable operation.

Since the cryosar is only a two-terminal element, the store is word organized with the bias voltage applied via the word conductors. To write the word is cleared by reducing the bias to zero and switching all the elements to the high-resistance state. Coincident voltages, positive on the word and negative on the digit conductors, are required to switch an element to the low-resistance, or 1, state. Reading is carried out destructively by the clear operation, or non-destructively by increasing the word voltage by an

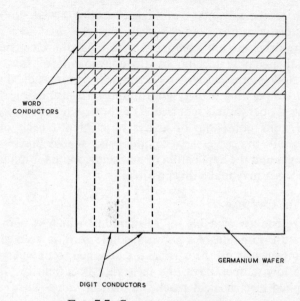

WORD CONDUCTORS

GERMANIUM WAFER

DIGIT CONDUCTORS

FIG. 7.7 *Cryosar storage array*

amount not sufficient to switch the elements, and detecting the change of current which occurs in the elements in the low-resistance state. Although it will operate in less than 10 nanoseconds and lends itself to mass fabrication, the cryosar has the disadvantage of requiring very low temperature refrigeration. The tunnel diode has very similar properties and, of course, operates at room temperature.

7.2 SUPERCONDUCTIVE STORAGE

In 1911 Kammerlingh-Onnes discovered that the electrical resistance of mercury suddenly disappeared when the metal was cooled to a temperature just below the boiling point of helium, $4.2°K$. The superconductive effect has been shown to exist in several metals including lead, tin, zinc, indium, tantalum and niobium. In addition, many compounds exhibit superconductivity. It has also been established that the presence of a magnetic field lowers the transition temperature at which the metal becomes superconducting. For any temperature which is less than the critical temperature of the material with no applied field, there is

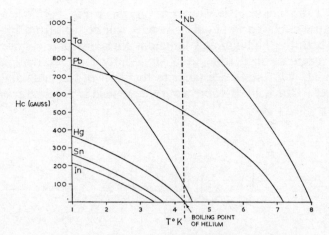

FIG. 7.8 *Critical magnetic field and temperature for some typical superconductors*

a threshold field above which the material is resistive and below which it is superconducting. As the temperature is decreased from the critical temperature, the magnetic field required to restore resistance to the material must be increased. The relation between the critical magnetic field and temperature is approximately parabolic, as shown in Fig. 7.8 for some typical metals. In addition to the property of zero resistance, it has been shown that a superconductor is a perfect diamagnetic substance in which the magnetic induction is zero until the threshold field is reached. This, result cannot be predicted from Maxwell's equations from which it is only possible to deduce that the magnetic induction cannot vary with time. Since the currents in a superconductor cannot flow strictly on the surface, there is a finite depth to which a magnetic field penetrates and in which the supercurrents flow. Because of the penetration depth, the observed threshold field for sufficiently thin superconducting films is greater than that for a large specimen. Since Buck described the 'cryotron',[13] a switching element making use of superconductive effects, several superconductive storage elements have been described. Elements based on the cryotron have also been developed.

7.2.1 THE CRYOTRON

The cryotron, as originally described, consists of a tantalum 'gate' wire around which a solenoid of niobium wire, usually named the 'control', is wound as shown in Fig. 7.9. When this structure is placed in liquid helium, it will be seen from Fig. 7.8 that both the niobium and tantalum wires are superconducting. The magnetic field, due to a sufficiently large current in the solenoid, will restore resistance to that part of the tantalum wire subject to the field. Because a very large field is required to make

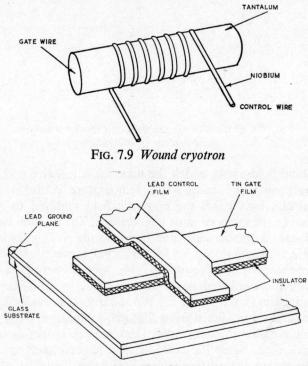

FIG. 7.9 *Wound cryotron*

FIG. 7.10 *Thin film cryotron*

niobium resistive at 4·2°K, the control wire is always super-conducting. The device, therefore, behaves as a four-terminal element in which the resistance between the gate terminals is controlled by a current applied to the control terminals. Although the maximum resistance in the gate wire is very low, the minimum resistance is zero, so that an infinite ratio is obtained. If a current is applied to a network of parallel branches, all except one of which are resistive, the current will take the path of zero resistance. It is thus possible to route a current through a network of cryotrons by making the selected path of zero resistance and all others resistive. Any conductor carrying a current is subject to the magnetic field due to the current; this limits the current which the gate wire can carry without becoming resistive. The current gain of a cryotron is defined as the ratio of maximum permissible gate current to the minimum control current required to make the gate resistive.

Much simpler cryotron structures have been developed,[14] which are suitable for large-scale fabrication by vacuum deposition techniques. One of these is shown in Fig. 7.10. In the crossed film cryotron the gate and control conductors are thin films of tin and lead respectively. These are deposited on a superconducting ground plane to reduce spreading of the magnetic field at the edges of the films. The current gain of this structure is a function of the ratio of the widths of the gate and control films and also of the depth to which a magnetic field penetrates a superconductor. A cryotron's switching time depends on the time constant of the element which is given by the ratio of the inductance

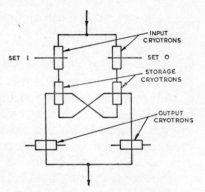

FIG. 7.11 *Cryotron arrangement storing one binary digit*

of the conductors to the resistance of the gate when normal. The geometry of the thin-film cryotron reduces the time constant and so faster operation is possible than with the original wound device. To reduce the time constant still further, the resistance of the gate may be increased by employing an in-line structure. In this element the gate and control run in parallel, thus increasing the length of conductor in which resistance is restored.

Cryotron arrays have been used for storage as well as for logical and switching operations.[16] Figure 7.11 is an arrangement of cryotrons for storing one binary digit. If the input current flows in the left-hand branch, it must also flow in the control of the right-hand storage cryotron, the gate of which is therefore held resistive. Current is then forced to flow in the left-hand branch and the condition is stable. The circuit has two stable states with current flowing in one or other of the two branches. To set the circuit to a known state, resistance is introduced into one branch by applying a control current to one of the input cryotrons, thus forcing the supply current to flow in the other branch. The state of the element is sensed by means of the output cryotrons, only one of which is resistive. A cryotron store has been proposed, and a small model demonstrated,[17] for 'associative addressing' in which all the words contained in the store are simultaneously compared with the required word and an indication given if this is contained in the store. This facility would be advantageous for storing catalogue or file information but cannot easily be provided by any other storage element. Because of its complexity and low packing density, the cryotron-type circuit is not very attractive for random-access storage and much simpler elements have been suggested to meet this requirement.

7.2.2 PERSISTENT-CURRENT STORAGE CELLS

When a circulating current is established in a superconductor, it will continue to flow indefinitely, until destroyed by some external means. Several geometries have been suggested for storage elements in which a binary digit is stored as the sense of a persistent current set up in a superconductor. The operation of all these elements depends on the application of a magnetic field which exceeds the threshold field, thus causing part of the super-conducting circuit to become resistive. The introduction of resistance allows the flux linking the circuit to change and sets up persistent currents (or, in other words, traps the flux change which occurs) when the applied field is removed.

7.2.3 TWO-HOLE STORAGE CELL

One of the first elements tried, described by Crowe in 1957,[19] consists of two D-shaped holes in a superconducting plane as shown in Fig. 7.12(a). The drive conductors run in parallel along one side of the bridge and the sense conductor on the other side as illustrated in Fig. 7.12(b). Consider the operation of the element when the drive current increases in the drive conductor; an equal and opposite current is induced in the superconduct-ing bridge until this current reaches the critical value at which the bridge becomes resistive. Provided that the temperature of the bridge is not increased by the heat generated when it is resistive, the current in the bridge then decays to the critical value where it remains until the end of the drive-current pulse. At the end of the drive pulse, an equal change is induced in the bridge, leaving a

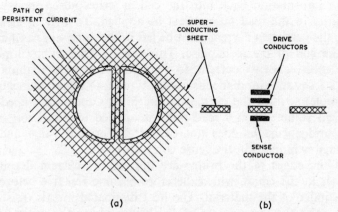

(a) *plan-view*   (b) *cross-section*

FIG. 7.12 *Persistent-current storage element*

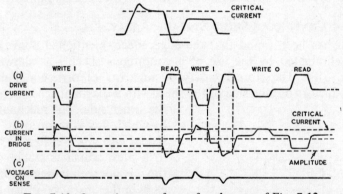

FIG. 7.13 *Operating waveforms for element of Fig. 7.12*

persistent current flowing in the opposite sense to that initially induced by the drive current. To read the information stored in the cell, a drive current of the opposite polarity is applied. This causes the current in the bridge to increase negatively until the bridge becomes resistive and the sense conductor, which is normally perfectly screened from the drive, by the superconducting bridge, is coupled to the drive. An output voltage as shown in Fig. 7.13(c) is induced in the sense conductor. The removal of the read-current sets up a persistent current in the opposite sense. To write information back into the cell, a write pulse, opposite in polarity to the read pulse, must be applied. To write 0 into the cell, the persistent current must be left in the same sense as it exists at the end of the read pulse. This can be achieved by limiting the effective drive current to half the amplitude required to write 1 (by the simultaneous application of an inhibit current, for example) so that the current in the bridge does not exceed the critical value. When a read pulse is applied to a cell storing 0, the bridge current does not exceed the critical value and no voltage is induced in the sense conductor.

If the edges of the bridge are diffuse, the current density is higher at the edges, which therefore become resistive before the remainder of the material. The heat dissipated in this resistance may raise the temperature of the bridge above the critical temperature of the material and the bridge becomes completely resistive. Because of variations in the edges, the critical current for the bridge is not reproducible and it is difficult then to fabricate an array with a large number of cells with the necessary uniformity.

7.2.4 CONTINUOUS-SHEET STORAGE ARRAY

It has been found that the edge effects mentioned above can be eliminated by the use of a continuous sheet,[21] as shown in Fig. 7.14. The store consists of an array of orthogonal drive conductors on one side of the sheet with a diagonal sense wire on the other side. The mechanism, by which flux is trapped or persistent currents continue to flow in a path which is stable with time, is not well understood. To explain the operation of the cell, it is assumed that the action of the drive currents is to set up small resistive areas near the intersection of the conductors, and that the magnetic field, due to persistent currents flowing round these areas, maintains them resistive. The cell then operates in a similar way to a two-hole element in which the resistive areas serve the same

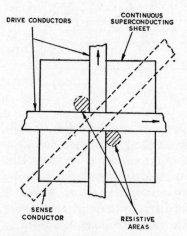

FIG. 7.14 *Continuous-sheet trapped-flux storage element*

purpose as holes. The magnetic fields due to equal currents flowing in the conductors, in the directions shown in Fig. 7.14, add in the areas shown as resistive but cancel in the other two quadrants. If the magnetic field is strong enough, the areas become resistive and persistent currents are set up. Operation of the cell is then identical to the operation of the two-hole cell previously described.

The continuous-sheet store is fabricated by multiple-layer vacuum deposition of superconducting metals and insulating layers on to a glass substrate. Firstly a tin ground plane is deposited then a silicon monoxide insulating layer and, thirdly, the sense conductor followed by another silicon monoxide layer. The fifth layer is the tin storage plane with an insulating layer on top. The X and Y conductors, separated by another insulating layer, are then deposited and the array protected by a final layer of silicon monoxide. All the conductors are lead films which are always superconducting at the operating temperature. The critical temperature of tin is $3.7°K$ and if the temperature is maintained just below this point low drive currents only are required. Successful operation with currents as low as 30 milliamps has been reported. It is claimed that good uniformity among the elements of an array can be achieved so that the system is suitable for two-coordinate selection. Linear packing densities as high as 200 per inch appear feasible.

7.2.5 THE PERSISTOR AND PERSISTATRON

Two other types of persistent-current storage cell have been described, the 'persistor'[23] and the 'persistatron'[24] which have very similar modes of operation. The persistor, Fig. 7.15, consists essentially of an inductor, made of a metal which is always super-conducting at the operating temperature, in parallel with a resistive element whose critical temperature is slightly greater than the working temperature. When a current pulse, which is twice the critical current of the resistive element, is applied to the cell, all the current change will take place through R which has negligible inductance compared with L. R therefore becomes resistive and a potential drop appears across L in which current begins to flow. The current increases in L and decreases in R until it reaches the critical current. When the current pulse is terminated, the current decreases in R, which again becomes superconducting, and a persistent current, equal to the critical current, is left circulating through L and R. A second current pulse of the same polarity as the first does not cause R to become resistive and does not change the state of the persistor. On the other hand, a current pulse of opposite polarity sets up a persistent current which circulates through L and R in the opposite direction. The persistor can therefore be used as a storage element, in which the sense of the persistent current represents the digits 0 and 1. The voltage drop which appears across R when it becomes resistive can be utilized to read out the stored information.

The persistatron, shown in Fig. 7.16, consists of two parallel superconducting paths, of differing lengths and, therefore, of unequal inductance, between the input terminals. When a current pulse is applied to the device, the current divides in the two

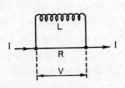

FIG. 7.15 *The 'persistor'*   FIG. 7.16 *The 'persistatron'*

branches inversely as the ratio of the inductances of the branches. The current in the shorter branch, I_1, will therefore be greater than the current in the other branch, I_2. As the input current increases, I_1 eventually reaches the critical current and the branch becomes resistive, resulting in any further increase taking place in I_2. When the input current pulse ends, both I_1 and I_2 decrease, the shorter branch again becomes superconducting and a persistent current is left circulating. It will thus be seen that the operation of the element is very similar to the persistor already described.

7.2.6 ADVANTAGES AND DISADVANTAGES OF SUPERCONDUCTIVE STORAGE

The major disadvantage of superconductive storage is the need for a closed-cycle liquid helium refrigerator.[25] Unless the cost of the refrigerator is spread over a large number of bits, a low-temperature system is not likely to be economic. However, it is claimed that the continuous-sheet superconductive store is inherently noise-free, because of the perfect screening effect of the superconducting sheet between sense and drive conductors. If this is so, then the capacity of such a store will not be limited by the same considerations as apply in the case of magnetic elements. With packing densities as high as 40000 per square inch, compact large-capacity systems may be manufactured. Switching time is low, less than 10 nanoseconds has been quoted, so that the same element may be used in high-speed, small-capacity systems. The use of cryotrons for selection may reduce the cost and make large systems very economic. Although cryotrons can be used for logic and a complete superconductive machine appears possible,[26] the adoption of the superconductive store need not depend on the success of cryotron logic. A self-contained system, consisting of both very large-capacity storage and smaller high-speed units which share the same refrigerator equipment, might provide all the storage required in an otherwise conventional machine.

BIBLIOGRAPHY

NEGATIVE-RESISTANCE STORAGE ELEMENTS

1. Couffignal, L. 'Le Machine de l'Institut Blaise Pascal'. Report on Conference on High-speed Automatic Calculating Machines held at the University Mathematical Laboratory, Cambridge, England, June, 1949, p. 65.

2. Raphael, M. S. and Robinson, A. S. 'Digital Storage Using Neon Tubes', *Electronics*, **29**, pp. 162–5 (July, 1956).

3. Richards, R. K. *Digital Computer Components and Circuits*, Van Nostrand (New York, 1957), p. 411.

4. Hurley, R. B. *Transistor Logic Circuits*, Wiley (New York, 1961).

5. Esaki, L. 'New Phenomenon in Narrow Ge. Pn Junctions', *Phys. Review*, **109** (2), pp. 603–4 (Jan. 15, 1958).

6. Beck, E. R., Savitt, D. A. and Whiteside, A. E. 'Tunnel Diode Storage Using Current Sensing', *Proc. Western Joint Computer Conference*, May, 1961, pp. 427–42.

7. Kaufman, M. M. 'Tunnel Diode Tenth Microsecond Memory', *I.R.E. International Convention Record*, 1960, Part 2, pp. 114–23.

8. Berry, D. L. and Fisch, E. A. 'High-speed Tunnel Diode Memory', *Digest of Technical Papers*, International Solid-State Circuits Conference held at Philadelphia, February, 1961, pp. 112–13.

9. Chaplin, G. B. B. and Thompson, P. M. 'A Fast Word-organized Tunnel-diode Memory Using Voltage-mode Selection', *Digest of*

Technical Papers, International Solid-State Circuits Conference held at Philadelphia, February, 1961.

10. Takahashi, S., Ishii, O., Nakazawa, K. and Murata, K. 'A Tunnel Diode High-speed Memory', *Proc. I.F.I.P. Congress*, 1962 held in Munich, Sept. 1962. North-Holland Publishing Company (Amsterdam 1963).

11. Cole, A. J., Chaplin, G. B. B. and Thompson, P. M. 'The Engineering of a Fast Word-organized Tunnel Diode Store', *Digest of Technical Papers*, International Solid-State Circuits Conference held at Philadelphia, Feb. 1962, pp. 40–1.

12. Macwhorter, A. L. and Rediker, R. H. 'The Cryosar—A New Low-temperature Computer Component', *Proc. I.R.E.*, **47**, pp. 1207–13 (1959).

SUPERCONDUCTIVE STORAGE

13. Buck, D. A. 'The Cryotron-superconductive Computer Component', *Proc. I.R.E.*, **44**, pp. 482–93 (1956).

14. Newhouse, V. L. and Bremer, J. W. 'High-speed Super-conductive Element for Two-dimensional Fabrication', *Jour. Applied Physics*, **30**, pp. 1458–9 (1959).

15. Newhouse, V. L., Bremer, J. W. and Edwards, H. H. 'An Improved Film Cryotron and Its Application to Digital Computers', *Proc. I.R.E.*, **48**, pp. 1395–1404 (1960).

16. Slade, A. E. and McMahon, H. O. 'A Cryotron Catalog Memory System', *Proc. Eastern Joint Computer Conference*, December, 1956, pp. 115–19.

17. Slade, A. E. and Smallman, C. R. 'Thin Film Cryotron Catalog Memory', *Proc. Symposium on Superconductive Techniques for Computing Systems* held at Washington D.C., May, 1960, pp. 213–29 (Office of Naval Research Symposium Report No. ACR–50).

18. Beesley, J. P. 'An Evaporated Film 135-Cryotron Memory Plane', *Digest of Technical Papers* presented at the International Solid-State Circuits Conference held at Philadephia, Feb. 1961, pp. 108–9.

19. Crowe, J. W. 'Trapped Flux Superconducting Memory', *I.B.M. Jour. Research and Development*, **1**, pp. 294–304 (1957).

20. Garwin, R. L. 'An Analysis of a Persistent Current Superconducting Memory Cell', *I.B.M. Jour. Research and Development*, **1**, pp. 304–8 (1957).

21. Burns, L. L., Alphonse, G. A. and Leck, G. W. 'Coincident-current Superconductive Memory', *Trans. I.R.E. on Electronic Computers*, **EC–10** (3), pp. 438–46 (1961).

22. Rhoderick, E. H. 'Low Temperature Storage Elements', *Jour. Brit. I.R.E.*, **20**, pp. 37–40 (1960).

23. Crittenden, E. C., Cooper, J. N. and Schmidlin, F. W. 'The Persistor—A Superconducting Memory Element', *Proc. I.R.E.*, **48**, pp. 1233–46 (1960).

24. Vail, C. R., Lucas, M. S. P., Owen, H. A. and Stewart, W. C. 'An Approach to the Experimental Study of Persistent-current Devices', *Proc. Symposium on Superconductive Techniques for Computing Systems* held at Washington D.C., May, 1960, pp. 56–74 (Office of Naval Research Symposium Report No. ACR–50).

25. Rose-Innes, A. C. 'Refrigeration of a Superconducting Memory for a Computer', *Brit. Jour. Applied Physics*, **10**, pp. 452–4 (1959).

26. Maguire, I. 'All-superconductive Computers—Commonplace in Ten Years? New Approaches to Memory Design', *Electronics*, **34**, No. 47, p. 45 (Nov. 24th, 1961).

CHAPTER 8

NON-ERASABLE STORAGE

IN MANY applications, a non-erasable store, in which the information is retained permanently, is acceptable and, in some cases, may have definite advantages, especially where security against loss of the stored information is important. The terms, non-erasable, permanent or semi-permanent, fixed and read-only are strictly relative, but all are used to qualify systems in which the information cannot be changed electrically. In any store it must be possible to write but, since this is carried out by some mechanical operation such as the insertion of plugs or cards, the writing time is many orders of magnitude longer than the reading time. Since the information is permanent, there is no write phase in the access cycle which may, therefore, be considerably shorter than the cycle in a conventional destructive read-out store. In addition to this advantage of shorter cycle time, the access and digit circuits tend to be less complex and consequently less expensive.

Like many other design features which are incorporated in the modern digital computer, the idea of using a permanent storage mechanism for storing instructions and tabular data originated with Babbage. In his plans for the Analytical Engine, he proposed to adapt the mechanism, invented by Jacquard at the beginning of the nineteenth century, for the weaving of fabrics with complicated patterns. In the Jacquard loom, the warp threads, which must be lifted before the passage of the shuttle, are specified by a pattern of holes punched in a card. These cards, one for each passage of the shuttle, are strung together to control the sequence in which the threads are lifted. In proposing a similar mechanism to control the operation of the Analytical Engine, Babbage preceded by nearly a century the actual use of punched cards or tape for storing the programme of instructions to a computer.

136

The operation of the early electromechanical automatic computers was controlled by punched-paper tapes, which is, of course, a form of non-erasable store, although now only used as an input and output medium. Instructions and constants were set up in the ENIAC by switches and by making connections via plugs and sockets. Since non-erasable storage is often cheaper and faster than conventional systems, its use for storing frequently used standard sub-routines (or sequences of instructions to carry out complex operations) and constants, may be advantageous. A fixed store for sub-routines, based on gas tubes and electro-mechanical relays, was first incorporated in the Model VI relay computer, built at Bell Telephone Laboratories. More recently, fixed stores have been employed for storing all the control information required to carry out the various instructions (or micro-programme) in several electronic computers.

Fixed stores may be considered as mechanisms which translate an input code into a different output code. In this guise they have been used in automatic telephone systems for many years, to translate the decimal digits dialled by the subscriber into a form suitable for setting up the selector switches in the exchange. A code translator always performs the two functions of decoding and encoding. The decoding operation reduces the input code to the fundamental 1 out of n possibilities which it specifies while the encoder recodes the n outputs from the decoder into the m outputs of the required code. A system for translating an n-digit binary code to an arbitrary output code of m digits is shown in Fig. 8.1. The decoder is, of course, similar to the address decoding

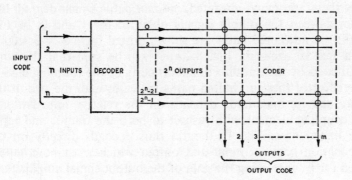

FIG. 8.1 *Code translator for n binary digit input code to arbitrary output code*

and selection circuits of a conventional random-access store and the same design principles may be applied (*see* Chapter 9). In the encoder, the input lines from the decoder are coupled to the output lines where a 1 is required in the output code. The circles at the intersections of the wires in the matrix of Fig. 8.1 indicate where coupling elements might be placed in a typical case. Non-linear coupling elements, such as diodes, have advantages but their cost rules out their use in large-capacity systems where they may be replaced by linear elements. Since, however,

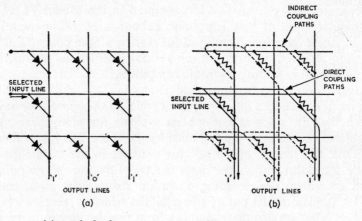

(*a*) *with diodes*   (*b*) *with linear elements*

FIG. 8.2 *Encoding array*

these are bi-directional, between any input line and the output lines there are many unwanted, indirect paths which degrade the ratio between the output signals obtained for 1 and 0. In Fig. 8.2(*b*) the unwanted paths are shown dotted for a 3 × 3 section of a matrix, while in Fig. 8.2(*a*) it will be seen that these are eliminated by the uni-directional property of the coupling diodes. The effect of these unwanted paths increases with the size of the array and its magnitude depends on the relative impedance of the coupling element with respect to both the output and input line impedances. The 1 : 0 ratio thus depends directly on the attenuation between input and output which must be compensated for by increasing the gain of the output signal amplifiers.

8.1 ARRAYS OF LINEAR COUPLING ELEMENTS

The use of discrete coupling elements connected at the required intersections in the matrix, although quite practicable, is not desirable for large capacities. Capacitive and inductive coupling have the advantage that no physical connections need be made at the intersections in the matrix. This simplifies fabrication and makes possible the insertion of data automatically by punching holes in metal cards. In addition, the system can be designed to facilitate changing the stored information rapidly by the removal of a card and the insertion of another, on which the new information has been punched. Some of the geometrical arrangements which have been used are described below.

8.1.1 CAPACITIVELY COUPLED ARRAYS

In all capacitively coupled arrays the arrangement consists of two orthogonal sets of conductors in which the capacitance between the conductors is normally very low but can be increased at the intersections where it is required to store 1. In the arrangement of Fig. 8.3 the capacitance at the intersections is between two circular electrodes, one on either side of a thin dielectric film. All the electrodes in one column on one side of the film are connected to a single-word conductor. Thus initially a 1 is stored at every intersection. To write 0 the connection between an electrode and the word line is broken by punching a hole as shown in Fig. 8.3.

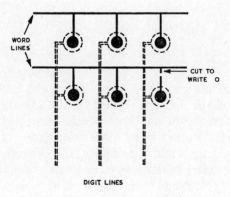

FIG. 8.3 *Capacitively coupled array*

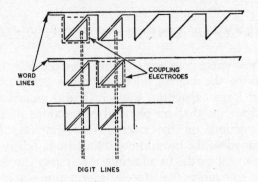

FIG. 8.4 *Alternative capacitively coupled array*

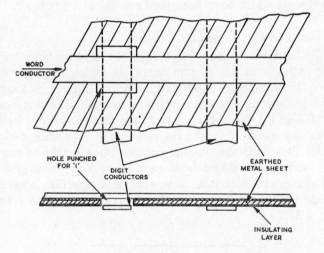

FIG. 8.5 *Capacitively coupled array with electrostatic screening*

A different method of varying the capacitance is shown in Fig. 8.4. Here the capacitor electrodes at the intersections are triangular in shape and are formed on the same side of the dielectric support. Again one electrode is connected to the word conductor and the other to the digit conductor but, in this case, the geometry is such that the capacitance between them is very low and 0 is stored initially at each intersection. To write 1, a square coupling electrode is placed over both triangular electrodes but insulated from them so that the three electrodes form two capacitors in series between the word and digit conductors. The coupling electrodes are mounted on a strip of insulating material (code strip) which can be replaced to change the information stored in one word.

A third method of varying the capacitance at the cross-points in the matrix is shown in Fig. 8.5. The word and digit conductors are assembled on either side of an insulated conducting sheet which is connected to earth. This earth plane thus forms an electrostatic screen between the conductors so that the coupling capacitance is very low. Where a 1 is required to be stored, a hole is punched in the electrostatic screen and the coupling capacitance is considerably increased.

The conductor arrangement may be fabricated by conventional photo-etched printed-circuit techniques in all the above systems. The packing densities which have been achieved range from four per square inch for the triangular electrode system[2] to the packing density of a standard punched card for which the system of Fig. 8.5 has been adapted, of some thirty per square inch. The cycle time of all these systems depends on the capacity of the store but using the arrangement of Fig. 8.3, a cycle time of 3 microseconds has been reported for a capacity of 1024 words each of 34 bits.[1] It has been estimated that the arrangement with the punched electrostatic screen could operate at a cycle time of $0\cdot1$ microseconds for a capacity of 10^4 bits while 10^7 bits would require a cycle time of 10 microseconds.[3]

8.1.2 INDUCTIVELY COUPLED ARRAYS

In all the inductively coupled arrays described below, the mutual inductance between orthogonal sets of word and digit conducting loops is increased at the cross-points in the matrix where 1 is stored. One of the first stores to be described, utilizing this form of coupling, is shown in Fig. 8.6. The coupling between the mutually perpendicular word and digit loops is very low at each intersection in the absence of any coupling elements. However, if a small ferromagnetic rod is inserted as shown, where coupling is required, the resulting increase in magnetic flux due to a current in the word wire increases the coupling considerably. To avoid cross-coupling between adjacent rods, extra rods, known as 'keeper' rods, are inserted as shown. These provide a return path for the flux from the coupling rods and so prevent the flux returning through coupling rods in adjacent words. In addition to reducing cross-coupling, the keeper rods increase the coupling for a stored 1 and make possible an increase in packing density. The array is fabricated by weaving insulated copper wires into a mesh and inserting ferrite rods, 1 mm in diameter and 6 mm long, in the required positions. The fixed store of the Ferranti ATLAS computer,[5] which is based on the above principle, has a cycle time of 0·4 microseconds for a capacity of 8192 words each of 50 bits. The packing density is some 80 bits per square inch.

In the 'EDDYCARD' store,[6] the coupling at the intersections in the array is increased by introducing a conducting loop as shown in Fig. 8.7. The drive current induces eddy currents in the conducting loop as shown and these currents, in turn, induce an e.m.f. in the sense conductor. A variant of this principle is shown in Fig. 8.8,

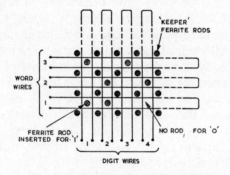

FIG. 8.6 *Ferrite-rod inductively coupled array*

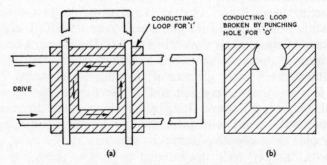

FIG. 8.7 *Principle of the 'Eddycard' inductively coupled store*

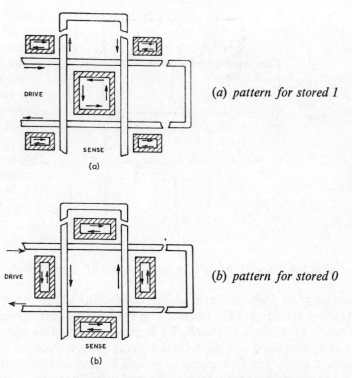

(a) *pattern for stored 1*

(b) *pattern for stored 0*

FIG. 8.8 *Alternative form of eddy-current coupling*

where 1 is represented by one pattern of coupling loops and 0 by the complementary pattern. This arrangement has the advantages of increasing the coupling between the drive and sense loops and of providing output signals of opposite polarity for 1 and 0, thus increasing the discrimination. However, it suffers from the disadvantage that either each stored bit must be inserted individually or, if cards with a number of coupling loops are used, each one must be printed with the coupling-loop configuration peculiar to its information pattern. In the Eddycard system, on the other hand, the information cards are printed with all coupling loops present and the information is inserted by breaking the loop at those positions corresponding to a stored 0; this may be carried out by punching holes in the card at the appropriate places, as shown in Fig. 8.7(b).

In the 'UNIFLUXOR' system,[7] shown in Fig. 8.9, the coupling between the drive (word) and sense (digit) loops, is caused by the

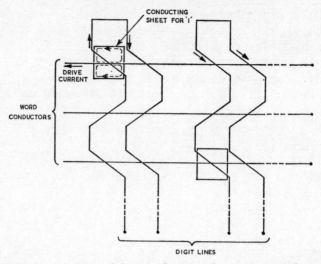

FIG. 8.9 *Principle of the 'Unifluxor' inductively coupled store*

eddy currents induced in a square conducting sheet or 'slug'. These are placed over the intersections in the array corresponding to positions where 1 is stored. To increase the coupling effect of the slug, the word and digit conductors no longer cross at right angles, but the e.m.f.s induced in a digit loop cancel when there is no slug present. An unbalanced word-conductor arrangement is used with the drive current returning through a common return conductor.

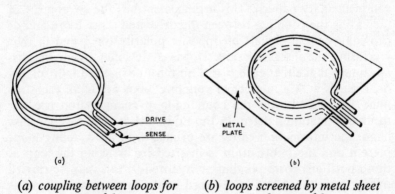

(a) *coupling between loops for   (b) loops screened by metal sheet*
stored 1   for stored 0

FIG. 8.10 *Principle of the inductively coupled array with eddy-current screening*

Eddy currents induced in a conducting sheet have the effect of reducing the mutual inductance between two loops, as illustrated in Fig. 8.10. When a conducting sheet is introduced as shown, the e.m.f. induced in the sense loop by a time-varying current in the drive loop is very much reduced. The coupling at the cross-points in an array of word and digit loops is, therefore, virtually eliminated by the insertion of a conducting sheet between them. If holes are punched in the sheet opposite intersections in the array corresponding to positions where 1 has to be stored, the drive current in a word line induces an e.m.f. only in the digit lines where a hole is present. The information can be changed easily, by inserting another conducting sheet, or card, on which the new information pattern has been punched.

8.2 PERMANENTLY WIRED TRANSFORMER-COUPLED SYSTEMS

If ease of changing the stored information is not a requirement, a very compact non-erasable store can be realized with conventional transformer coupling between input and output. The arrangement is illustrated in Fig. 8.11, in which there is one transformer core, shown for simplicity as a toroid, for each digit in the word. The information is stored by the pattern in which the word wires, one for each word, thread these cores. Where the digit in a word is 1, the word wire threads the corresponding core but bypasses the cores where the digits are 0's. Thus, when a pulse is applied to the selected word wire, an e.m.f. is induced in the digit-winding

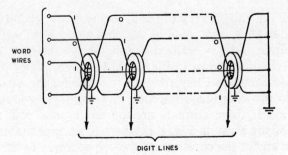

WORD
WIRES

DIGIT LINES

FIG. 8.11 *Permanently wired transformer-coupled store*

on those cores through which the word wire passes. An output signal appears, therefore, on the digit lines corresponding to stored 1's and there is no output on the lines corresponding to the 0's in the word.

For large capacities using the above arrangement, the bulk of the equipment is in the address decoding and selection circuits

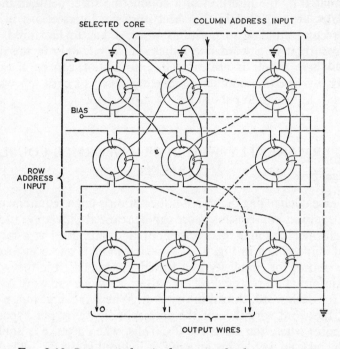

Fig. 8.12 *Permanently wired, rectangular-loop core array*

which are not shown. Any of the decoding and selection methods described in Chapter 9 could be used but a considerable saving of total equipment can be realized by using the switch-core selection-matrix technique shown in Fig. 8.12. The principle of operation is fully described in Chapter 9 but, essentially, the operation is similar to two-coordinate selection in a rectangular-loop ferrite-core array. If drive currents are applied to one row and one column of the array in Fig. 8.12, there is no appreciable change of flux in any of the cores except the one common to the selected row and column. The selected core is returned to its original state by the bias current which is common to every core in the array.

A secondary winding on each core in the array could provide the drive to the word wires in the transformer arrangement of Fig. 8.11, but the extra transformer cores are not necessary. A particular digit wire can be threaded directly through those cores in the array where the output word has a 1 in the corresponding digit position. This makes for a very compact system in which, however, the information cannot easily be changed. A store of this type has been used to store the sequencing information in the control unit of EDSAC 2.[12] This unit has a capacity equivalent to 1024 words, each of some 100 bits, and a cycle time of 1·5 microseconds.

8.3 SYSTEMS BASED ON ERASABLE STORAGE TECHNIQUES

Information can be permanently stored in most erasable storage systems which employ discrete elements by removing those elements which correspond to a stored 0. This may have

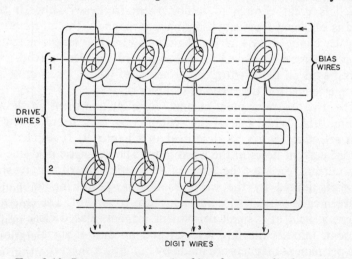

FIG. 8.13 *Permanent store using biased rectangular-loop cores*

advantages in applications where both erasable and non-erasable storage is required, because the same access and digit circuits can be shared by both stores. Since a sufficiently large bias current, threading a rectangular-loop core in the direction opposing the read drive, inhibits switching, it is possible to remove a core electrically by threading a bias wire through it. In the diagram of Fig. 8.13, with two sets of cores, eight words are stored by the threading pattern of four bias wires. For example, word number 1 is selected by applying a current to drive wire number 1 while the bias current is applied to bias wire number 1, giving 010 as the first three digits in the output word. If the bias is now applied to bias wire number 2, the second word is selected giving 100 for the first three digits. Obviously, if all four bias wires thread the same core, it may be omitted, so that the maximum number of bias wires threading a single core is reduced to three. This arrangement is an extension of the transformer system of Fig. 8.11 where an extra level of selection has been introduced using the non-linear properties of a rectangular-loop core. A sub-routine store using this principle has been operating successfully for some years.[13]

Arrangements have also been used where the information is inserted into a conventional core matrix, by subjecting those cores in which 0 is to be stored, to an external magnetic field which is great enough to inhibit them from switching. If the field is obtained from small permanent magnets, the information may be changed by altering their position. Permanent magnets have also been employed to realize a card-changeable read-only store based on the twistor, the principle of which, as an erasable storage element, is described in Chapter 6.

The twistor permanent-magnet store arrangement is shown in Fig. 8.14. When one of the switch cores (which are arranged in a selection matrix as described in Chapter 9) is selected, an output current flows in the word loop. The magnetic field due to this current reverses the state of magnetization of the twistor elements linked by the word conductor, producing an e.m.f. between each twistor wire and its return conductor. The external magnetic field of a small permanent magnet, placed close to an element, inhibits the flux reversal and no output signal results. The permanent magnets are made by bonding a sheet of magnetic material, which is suitable for permanent magnets, to an aluminium card. Small bar magnets are then formed, in every bit position, by photo-etching techniques. The magnets in positions corresponding to a stored 0 are then magnetized and the card inserted so that the magnets are close to the twistor elements. The information can be changed by demagnetizing all the magnets

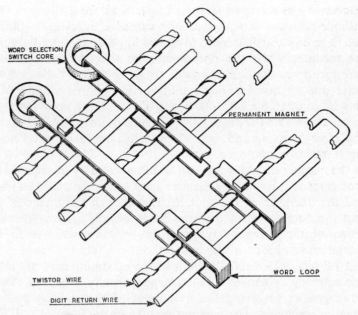

FIG. 8.14 *Permanent-magnet twistor store*

on a card and remagnetizing those corresponding to 0 in the new information pattern. A store of 4096 words, each of 88 bits, has been described;[15] it has a cycle time of 5 microseconds.

8.4 SYSTEMS USING OPTICAL TECHNIQUES

Since the inherent resolution of a photographic emulsion is very high, its use as a non-erasable large-capacity store, in which the information is stored as a pattern of opaque and transparent areas, appears very attractive. Although a packing density greater than 10^8 per square centimetre is theoretically possible, this is considerably reduced by practical considerations. One of the main problems which must be overcome before photographic techniques can be applied, is that of gaining access to the stored information. Reading must be carried out optically, which involves the selective illumination of the required area and detecting the light transmitted through the film or plate. The access arrangements thus involve the relative motion of the light source with respect to the storage medium. Light, both from the spot of a cathode-ray tube, which is usually named a flying-spot scanner, and from an electroluminescent matrix has been used to illuminate the medium while the photomultiplier tube forms a suitable detector. Since the light available from the source is limited, the noise due to random fluctuations in the photomultiplier tube may be comparable with the signal. The resulting poor signal-to-noise ratio makes the probability of reading-errors quite significant and error-detecting and -correcting techniques, using extra parity digits, must be employed.

The number of bits which can be illuminated by a single flying-spot scanner is limited by the area over which the spot can move and the diameter of the spot itself. Although the image of the spot can be enlarged or reduced by an optical system, the resolution of the scanning system is not thereby increased. The maximum resolution of the best cathode-ray tubes is between 10^6 and 10^7 bits, which sets the limit to the maximum capacity using one scanning system. If a much larger capacity is needed, access arrangements involving the movement of the storage medium must be employed. The medium may be in the form of a disc, a drum or a strip of photographic film, which moves past a stationary reading position. This arrangement has the disadvantage that access to the information is now serial, but a combination of a flying-spot scanner and a moving storage medium would enable some of the advantages of both systems to be realized.

8.4.1 THE FLYING-SPOT STORE

The basic equipment required in the flying-spot reading system for photographic storage is illustrated in Fig. 8.15. The light from the spot is focussed on to the storage plate by the optical system, and, if the illuminated area of the emulsion is transparent, the transmitted light is detected by the photomultiplier tube. The most severe problem in this arrangement is the registration of the spot on any particular digit, which depends on the accuracy with which the deflection voltages can be defined and maintained during operation. This is much more severe than the allied problem in electrostatic storage tube systems (*see* Chapter 3) since the number of spots to be resolved is considerably greater. The system shown in Fig. 8.16 overcomes this difficulty of accurate positioning by an optical feedback method. Light from the spot is passed through a set of coded address masks, which are mounted in the

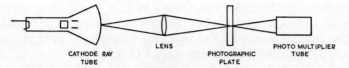

CATHODE RAY
TUBE

LENS

PHOTOGRAPHIC
PLATE

PHOTO MULTIPLIER
TUBE

FIG. 8.15 *Principle of the flying-spot photographic store*

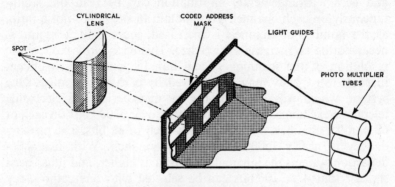

SPOT

CYLINDRICAL
LENS

CODED ADDRESS
MASK

LIGHT GUIDES

PHOTO MULTIPLIER
TUBES

FIG. 8.16 *Optical system for location of the spot in the
flying-spot store*

same plane as the information plate, as shown in the figure. The
outputs from the photomultiplier tubes, one of which is provided
to detect the light from each digit position in the mask, thus
represent the present address of the spot which is compared with
the input address. A signal, proportional to the difference between
the required and present address, is fed back to the deflection
plates of the cathode-ray tube, thus deflecting the beam to and
keeping it locked in the correct position. A similar optical system,
turned through a right angle, locates the beam in the other
coordinate direction. The difficulties of mechanical registration of
the information plate with the address masks are avoided by
employing the flying-spot scanner for writing the information as
well as reading. The unexposed plate is inserted into the system
and the beam deflected to every location where it is either turned
on or not, depending on the bit to be stored. After developing,
the plate is re-inserted and the information may then be read as
required. The address masks may be binary-coded, as shown in
Fig. 8.16 (where three digit levels are shown for simplicity), but if
the Gray, or reflected binary, code is used, gross positional errors
may be avoided. The Gray code has the property that only one

L

digit position changes value, from 0 to 1 or 1 to 0, in going from one level to the next, unlike the normal binary code in which many digit positions may change; for example, in going from 63 to 64, 6 digit positions change from 1 to 0.

Using parallel optical channels, each with its own lens, storage plate and photomultiplier tube but sharing one cathode-ray tube and access arrangements, information can be read out simultaneously on each channel. To maintain the signal-to-noise ratio, as the number of channels is increased, more light is required, necessitating an increase in spot size. This necessarily reduces the resolution of the scanning system but, in general, a significant increase in capacity may be achieved by parallel operation. One system, which was built for use in an experimental electronic telephone exchange,[18] has a capacity of over 32000 bits on each of 68 parallel channels or 32000 words each of 68 bits. The packing density is nearly 15000 bits per square inch. With magnetic-deflection systems the inherent resolution is higher, and it has been stated[19] that 4×10^6 bits can be selected with one cathode-ray tube.

8.4.2. ELECTROLUMINESCENT STORAGE TECHNIQUES

Light is emitted by certain phosphors when they are subjected to an alternating electric field. Such electroluminescent materials have found wide use for illuminated signs and have also been employed in a high-speed coordinate display unit, by means of which digital data may be plotted in graphical form. The electroluminescent matrix, on which this display unit is based, has been adapted as a selection mechanism for an optical-storage system. Figure 8.17 illustrates the method of assembly of a typical electroluminescent matrix. It consists of two orthogonal sets of conductors between which the phosphor layer is deposited. At each intersection of these X and Y conductors an electroluminescent cell is formed. One electrode is formed on a glass substrate, by vacuum deposition of a film of gold, thin enough to be transparent, so that light emitted from the cells is freely transmitted. The light output, L, from an electroluminescent phosphor, is a non-linear function of the applied voltage, V, and is given by

$$L = A \exp \left\{ -\frac{b}{\sqrt{(V)}} \right\}$$

where A and b are constants of the material. Therefore, if equal pulse voltages of opposite polarity are applied to one X and to one Y coordinate electrode, the light emitted by the cell at the intersection is many times greater than the light emitted by the remaining cells on the selected row and column. The information is stored as a pattern of holes in an opaque mask which is mounted so that the position of the holes is aligned with the electroluminescent cells.

When one cell is selected, the emitted light passes through a

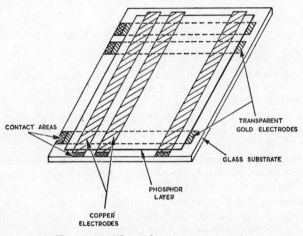

FIG. 8.17 *Electroluminescent matrix*

hole in the mask, representing a stored 1, and is detected by a photomultiplier tube. If there is no hole aligned with the selected cell, a stored 0, there is no output signal from the photomultiplier. The speed of operation of the matrix is limited by the afterglow from the phosphor and the number of cells in one array is limited by the ratio of the light flux from the selected cell to the flux from all the half-selected cells.

The discrimination between the wanted and unwanted light outputs from the array may be increased by applying sine-wave excitation of two differing frequencies to the X and Y coordinates, say f_1 to the X and f_2 to the Y coordinate. Due to the non-linear relationship between light output and applied voltage, a mixing action takes place in the selected cell and the component of the emitted light at the difference frequency $(f_1 - f_2)$, may be selected at the output from the photomultiplier. Since the light from half-selected cells consists of the input frequencies f_1 and f_2 or of their harmonics only, the discrimination is very considerably increased. A 128 × 128 array has been successfully demonstrated,[21] compared with the maximum permissible size of 32 × 32, using pulse operation. The cycle time of this prototype array is 100 microseconds but, since this is not limited by the phosphor afterglow, it is claimed that an improvement of at least a factor of 4 should be possible. The packing density achieved is some 2600 per square inch.

BIBLIOGRAPHY

LINEAR COUPLING ELEMENTS

1. Macpherson, D. H. and York, R. K. 'Semipermanent Storage by Capacitive Coupling', *Trans. I.R.E. on Electronic Computers*, EC–10, pp. 446–51 (1961).

2. Van Goethem, J. 'The Capacitive Semipermanent Information Store and Its Uses in Telephone Exchanges', *Proc. I.E.E.*, **107B**, Supplement No. 20, pp. 346–52 (1960).

3. Foglia, H. R., McDermid, W. L. and Petersen, H. E. 'Card Capacitor—A Semipermanent Read Only Memory', *I.B.M. Journal of Research and Development*, **5**, pp. 67–8 (1961).

4. Takahashi, S. and Watanabe, S. 'Capacitance Type Fixed Memory', *Large Capacity Memory Techniques for Computer Systems*, edited by M. C. Yovits, Macmillan and Co. (New York, 1962), pp. 53–62.

5. Kilburn, T. and Grimsdale, R. L. 'A Digital Computer Store with a Very Short Read Time', *Proc. I.E.E.*, **107B**, pp. 567–72 (1960).

6. Ishedate, T., Yoshizawa, S. and Nagamori, K. 'EDDY CARD Memory—A Semi-Permanent Storage', *Proc. Eastern Joint Computer Conference*, December, 1961, pp. 194–208.

7. Renard, A. M. and Neumann, W. J. 'UNIFLUXOR—A Permanent Memory Element', *Proc. Western Joint Computer Conference*, May, 1960, pp. 91–6.

8. Endo, I. and Yamato, J. 'The Metal Card Memory—A New Semi-permanent Store', *Large Capacity Memory Techniques for Computing Systems*, edited by M. C. Yovits. Macmillan and Co. (New York, 1962). pp. 213–30.

9. Yamato, J. and Suzuki, Y. 'Forming Semi-permanent Memories with Metal Card Storage', *Electronics*, **34**, pp. 136–41 (November 17th, 1961).

PERMANENTLY WIRED TRANSFORMER-COUPLED SYSTEMS

10. Dimond, T. L. 'The No. 5 Crossbar A.M.A. Translator', *Bell Lab. Record*, **29**, pp. 62–8 (1951).

11. Wier, J. M. 'A High-speed Permanent Storage Device', *Trans. I.R.E. on Electronic Computers*, EC-4, pp. 16-20 (1955).

12. Wilkes, M. V., Renwick, W. and Wheeler, D. J. 'The Design of the Control Unit of an Electronic Digital Computer', *Proc. I.E.E.*, 105B, pp. 121-8 (1958).

SYSTEMS BASED ON ERASABLE STORAGE TECHNIQUES

13. Renwick, W. 'A Magnetic-Core Matrix Store with Direct Selection Using a Magnetic-Core Switch Matrix', *Proc. I.E.E.*, 104B, Supplement No. 7, pp. 436-44 (1957).

14. Looney, D. H. 'A Twistor Matrix Memory for Semipermanent Information', *Proc. Western Joint Computer Conference*, March, 1959, pp. 36-41.

15. Barrett, W. A., Humphrey, F. B., Ruff, J. A. and Stadler, H. L. 'A Card-changeable Permanent-magnet Twistor Memory of Large Capacity', *Trans. I.R.E. on Electronic Computers*, EC-10, pp. 451-61 (1961).

OPTICAL TECHNIQUES

16. King, G. W., Brown, G. W. and Ridenour, L. N. 'Photographic Techniques for Information Storage', *Proc. I.R.E.*, 41, pp. 1421-8 (1953).

17. Hoover, C. W., Staehler, R. E. and Ketchledge, R. W. 'Fundamental Concepts in the Design of the Flying Spot Store', *Bell Systems Tech. Jour.* 37, pp. 1161-94 (1958).

18. Keister, W., Ketchledge, R. W. and Lovell, C. A. 'The Morris Electronic Telephone Exchange', *Proc. I.E.E.*, 107B, Supplement No. 20, pp. 257-63 (1960).

19. Bryan, J. S. and Focht, L. R. 'The Cathode Ray Tube as a Commutating Device in Large-Capacity Random-access Stores', *Large Capacity Memory Techniques for Computing Systems*, edited by M. C. Yovits. Macmillan and Co. (New York, 1962) pp. 99-115.

20. Hoffman, G. R., Smith, D. H. and Jeffreys, J. C. 'High-speed Light Output Signals from Electroluminescent Storage Systems', *Proc. I.E.E.*, 107B, pp. 599-605 (1960).

21. Hoffman, G. R. and Jones, P. L. 'An Electroluminescent Fixed Store for a Digital Computer', *Proc. I.E.E.*, 109B, pp. 177-83 (1962).

22. Linder, S. L. and Hoover, C. W. 'Improved Performance from Matrix Electroluminescent Screens in Optical Readout Applications', *Large Capacity Memory Techniques for Computing Systems*, edited by M. C. Yovits, Macmillan and Co. (New York, 1962), pp. 231-61.

GENERAL

23. Taub, D. M. 'A Short Review of Read Only Memories', *Proc. I.E.E.*, 110, pp. 157-66 (1963).

CHAPTER 9

ACCESS, DIGIT AND CONTROL CIRCUITS IN RANDOM-ACCESS SYSTEMS

THE access, digit and control circuits are each concerned with one of the interfaces between the store and the rest of the computer (or any other system) of which the store forms part. The access circuits interpret the address input; that is, the input to the store which labels an item of information. The digit circuits are concerned with the two-way transfer of information between the store and the computer, while the control circuits accept the commands from the computer and cause the correct sequence of operations to be carried out inside the store.

The basic concepts governing the design of these circuits for a store consisting of an array of discrete elements are independent of the actual storage medium employed. While the details of the circuit design obviously must depend on the characteristics of the storage element, the functions which must be carried out by these circuits are similar whether magnetic cores, thin magnetic films, tunnel diodes or any other elements are employed. Although some of the functions are not required in a non-erasable store, the same principles must be applied where the storage medium is an inductively or capacitively coupled array. The design principles can therefore be described without reference to any particular storage medium but any peculiarities introduced by the various storage elements will be mentioned where appropriate. In the vast majority of applications the digits in a word of information are transferred in parallel. Serial transfer is possible but may be looked upon as a special case of parallel transfer in which the word contains only one digit.

156

9.1 ACCESS CIRCUITS

The primary function of the access circuits is to locate the information specified by the input address. The input address is almost always given in some coded form, often pure binary or binary-coded decimal representation, and at the logic level, or level at which information is transferred within the system. The access circuits must, therefore, perform the necessary decoding operation and include any necessary amplification from the logic-signal level to the power level required by the storage elements. The selection of a word always involves the routing of a defined current or voltage via a selection switch to the wire or wires common to the elements in the word. In the simplest scheme, illustrated in Fig. 9.1, an active switch is provided for each line to be selected. If the address is coded in a 1 out of N representation, the switches are controlled directly by the N input lines. However, when the address is coded in binary, extra decoding must be carried out. Figure 9.2 shows a decoding tree consisting of a number of changeover switches whose position is controlled by the input binary address digits. The route from the input to one of the eight output terminals is uniquely determined by the binary digits. A similar tree-decoding scheme in which the switches are replaced by transistors is shown in Fig. 9.3. Here again the route followed by the input current is determined by the potential applied to transistor bases.

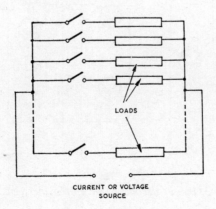

LOADS

CURRENT OR VOLTAGE
SOURCE

FIG. 9.1 *Direct selection arrangement*

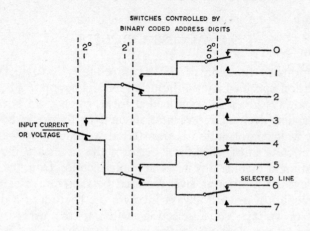

FIG. 9.2 *Binary decoding tree*

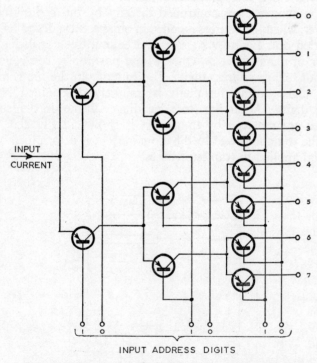

FIG. 9.3 *Binary decoding tree employing transistors*

In both of the above decoding arrangements, power gain is obtained from the switches or the transistors but, in general, the decoding and amplifying functions are provided separately. Although decoding may be carried out at logic level using standard logic circuits, it is often more economical to provide special decoding circuits employing diodes. Two arrangements are shown in Fig. 9.4; Fig. 9.4(a) is a diode tree-decoder in which the input voltage pulse is routed to one of the outputs, while Fig. 9.4(b) illustrates a decoder based on diodes connected as multi-input 'and' gates. The latter arrangement requires more diodes than the tree-decoder which, in general, requires $4(2^n - 1)$ diodes for n input digits; the multi-input 'and' gate system requires $2^n(n + 1)$ diodes, so that the saving in the number of diodes may be considerable for large n. However, when n is large, the total number of elements may be reduced, by performing the decoding at two or more levels. For example, decoding to two groups, each with 2^r outputs (r input binary digits) which are then combined in pairs, one from each group, gives a very significant reduction; 10 input digits, if decoded in this way, require two 5 input tree-decoders (248 diodes) for the first level and 2×1024 diodes for the second level, a total of 2296 diodes, compared with 4092 diodes for a single-level tree ($4\{2^{10} - 1\}$). This *combinatorial* method is very powerful for large n.

9.1.1 COMBINATORIAL SELECTION METHODS

The *direct selection* arrangement of Fig. 9.1 requires as many switches as there are lines to be selected and, since each switch has to provide power gain, it is usually a relatively expensive component. For large-capacity systems, therefore, economy demands that the number of switches required for selection be a minimum. The two-level decoding scheme described above may be applied to a *combinatorial selection* arrangement in which the second level of decoding is introduced after the power amplification has been carried out by the active switches. In this arrangement, both ends of the lines to be selected are connected in groups in such a way that only one line is directly connected to the source. Figure 9.5 shows sixteen lines connected in four groups of four at each end, reducing the number of switches required to eight. Because of the indirect paths which exist, one of which is shown in the figure, a diode must be inserted in each line to ensure that current flows only in the selected path. The minimum number of switches

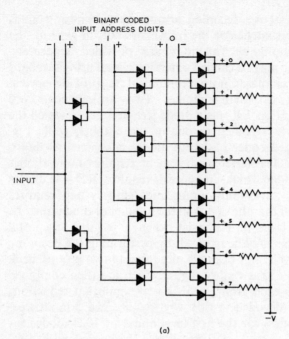

BINARY CODED
INPUT ADDRESS DIGITS

(a) Diode tree-
decoder

(a)

FIG. 9.4

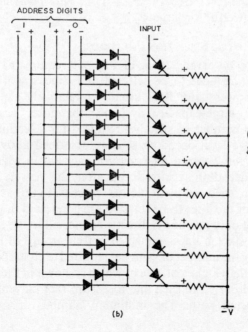

ADDRESS DIGITS

INPUT

(b) Parallel 'and'
gate diode decoder

(b)

required to select 1 out of N lines, is given by $2\sqrt{N}$, so that the reduction becomes appreciable for large capacities.

The single-diode array of Fig. 9.5 is only suitable for selection where a uni-directional current (or voltage) is required. Where bi-directional currents are required in the selection wires, as, for example, in a core store where the reading and writing currents are of opposite polarity, either two parallel but separate selection

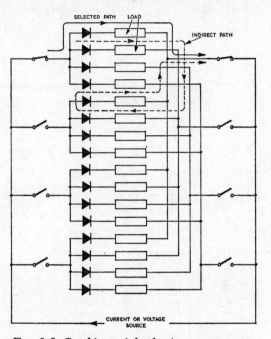

FIG. 9.5 *Combinatorial selection arrangement*

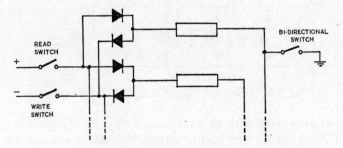

FIG. 9.6 *Selection array for bi-polar drive with bi-directional switches*

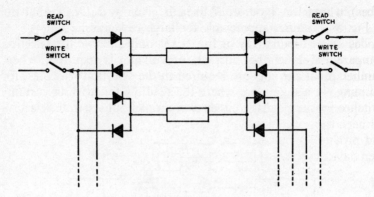

FIG. 9.7 *Selection array for bi-polar drive with uni-directional switches*

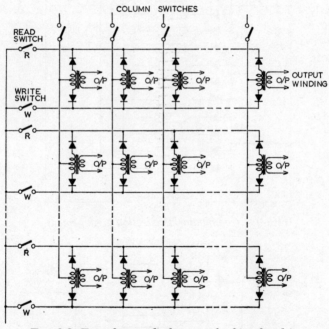

FIG. 9.8 *Transformer-diode array for bi-polar drive*

wires can be used with two selection arrays similar to Fig. 9.5, or, if the switches are bi-directional, by adding another set of diodes and switches as shown in Fig. 9.6. Usually the switches are uni-directional only (consisting of transistors or thermionic tubes), when more diodes and switches must be added, as shown in Fig. 9.7. This results in a fourfold increase in the number of diodes and a twofold increase in the number of switches when compared with the simple uni-directional arrangement. The number of diodes and switches may be reduced, if transformer coupling is employed,[2] as shown in Fig. 9.8, in which the column switches replace one set of read and write switches. The transformer also makes it easier to match the impedance of the load and provides a balanced drive to the selection lines, which need then have no common earth connection.

9.1.2   SWITCH-CORE SELECTION MATRIX

Coordinate selection in the three-dimensional magnetic-cor array, described in Chapter 5 and shown in Fig. 5.5, is essentially a combinatorial system in which the non-linear characteristic of the diodes is replaced by the non-linear characteristic of the rect-angular-loop cores. The natural extension of this leads to the *switch-core selection matrix* in which the cores are only used for selection. A 4×4 array, or matrix, is shown in Fig. 9.9 in which

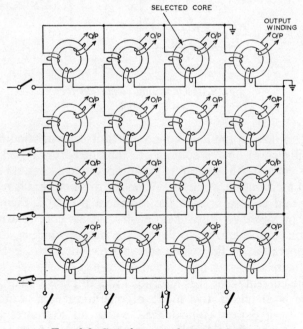

FIG. 9.9 *Switch-core selection matrix*

the output winding on each core is connected to one of the sixteen lines to be selected. In one mode of operation of this arrangement,[3] initially all the row switches are closed and the current flowing in the row windings biases all the cores to point B on the $\Phi - I$ characteristic in Fig. 9.10. To select one core, the current in the row on which the core is situated is turned off and the operating point for all the cores on that row moves to the remanent point A. If a drive current is now turned on in the column, the selected core moves to point C and the resulting flux change causes a

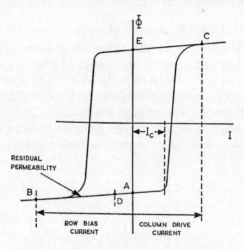

FIG. 9.10 *Operating conditions for switch cores*

current to flow in the load connected to its output winding. The remaining cores on the column are inhibited from switching by the row currents, the operating point moving to D, and no current flows in their output windings. When the drive current is removed the selected core returns to the remanent point, E. Finally, the current in the row is turned on again and the core returns to B causing a reverse current to flow in the output winding. Inherent in the operation of the switch-core matrix, therefore, is bi-polar drive; the read-current flows when the switch core is selected and the write-current when it is returned to its original state.

There is an alternative mode of operation of a switch-core matrix using current-coincidence,[1] where all the cores have a direct current bias applied in a separate winding, which holds the operating point at *B*. When drive currents are turned on simultaneously, in one row and one column, the sum of the drive currents links the core at the intersection and this core switches to point *C*. The other cores on the selected row and column move to a point near *A*, since they have only one drive current applied. This method of operation has the advantage that all the drive switches to the rows and columns are similar and are not required to pass current continuously. In the anti-coincident operation of the matrix in Fig. 9.9, the row switches, on the other hand, must be rated for continuous operation. The coincident-current system does require one extra winding for the bias current on each core.

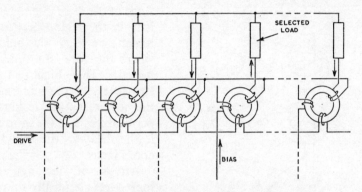

FIG. 9.11 '*Set-a-line*' *operation of switch-core matrix*

In 'set-a-line' operation of a switch-core matrix,[4] a bias current is first applied to the selected column, moving all the cores on the column from the remanent point, *A*, to point *B*, in Fig. 9.10. When a drive current is applied to the selected row, all the cores, other than the one with the bias applied, are switched to point *C*. If the output windings and loads are interconnected, as shown in Fig. 9.11, the e.m.f.s induced in the output windings cause equal currents to flow in the loads and these currents combine and return through the load connected to the unswitched core. Where there are *n* cores in a row, the ratio of the current flowing in the selected load to the current flowing in an unselected load is $n - 1 : 1$.

An inevitable delay occurs between the instant of turning on the drive currents in a switch-core matrix and the time when the output current reaches its nominal amplitude. This is mainly due to the inductance of the unselected cores in a row or column, which limits the rate at which the drive current can increase. Until the net current linking the selected core exceeds the critical current, I_c, the core does not start switching and no output current flows. Since the total inductance depends on the number of cores in a row or column, this delay can be embarrassingly long in a large matrix. The inductance of an unselected core depends on the number of turns on the drive winding and the residual slope of the $\Phi - I$ characteristic in the region between remanence and the point where the core is normally biased. The higher the squareness of the material, the lower is this residual permeability and the shorter is the delay in the switch-core matrix.

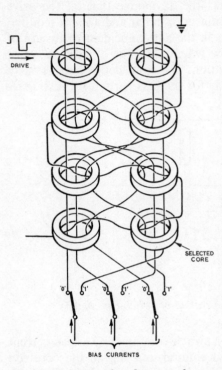

DRIVE

SELECTED CORE

BIAS CURRENTS

FIG. 9.12 *Binary decoding switch-core matrix*

Arrays of rectangular-loop cores are ideally suited for performing decoding and encoding operations. The threshold characteristic of the hysteresis loop makes them suitable for multi-input 'and' gate operation, while the output from different cores may be added logically, simply by threading a common wire through them. A three-binary digit decoding switch is shown in Fig. 9.12, for example. The winding pattern of the array of eight cores is such that, for any combination of the three input changeover switches, which are controlled by the binary digits to be decoded, only one core is unbiased. When the drive current is applied this core switches and induces an e.m.f. in any output winding which threads it. Since an output winding may thread any of the cores in the array, any logical function of the three input digits may be realized by the appropriate threading pattern. A limit to the number of input digits is set by the number of windings which can conveniently be put on a core. The coincident-current triangular array of Fig. 9.13 is suitable for decoding one decimal digit, represented by the combination of two 1's and three 0's on

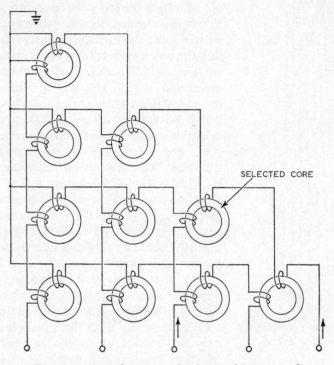

FIG. 9.13 *Decoding array for 2 out of 5 input code*

the five input lines, or 2 out of 5 code. This array can be extended to decode 2 out of *n* inputs, by adding further rows.

9.1.3 LOAD-SHARING MATRIX SWITCHES

In this class of matrix switches, the outputs from unselected cores are much reduced while the power from several input drivers is available at the output via the selected core, thus reducing the power required from each driver. The windings on the cores are so arranged that the m.m.f.s due to the input drive currents all augment each other on the selected core but cancel on all the unselected cores. To illustrate the principle of operation, an

M

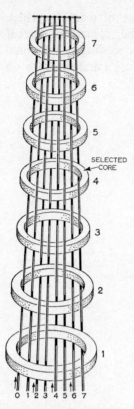

FIG. 9.14 *Load-sharing matrix switch*

8-input switch with 7 outputs is shown in Fig. 9.14. A core is selected by applying currents to 4 of the 8 inputs; for example, to select core number 4, drive currents must be applied to inputs 0, 2, 4 and 6, all of which thread core number 4 in the positive sense. In any other core, it will be seen that two of these windings link the core positively and two negatively so that no net m.m.f. is applied to the unselected cores. The wiring rules for the cores in an array with this property, which have been the subject of a considerable amount of theoretical investigation, are allied to the mathematical treatment of orthogonal matrices.[9, 12] Another type of load-sharing matrix can be constructed on the same lines as the multiple coincidence selection schemes for core arrays described in Section 5.1.5.[11] Since the number of input drivers required in all load-sharing matrices is always greater than the number of selected outputs, and since the practical difficulties in putting a large number of windings on a core are considerable, the principle can only be applied when the number of selection lines is fairly small. An added disadvantage is the increased complexity of the decoding circuits which are required to select the input drivers to the matrix.

9.1.4 COMPARISON OF THE RELATIVE COSTS OF SELECTION ARRANGEMENTS

Since the cost of the access circuits may be a significant fraction of the total cost of a complete storage system, it is useful to compare the relative cost of the different methods of selection which have been described. This cost comparison is based on the number of major components, namely switches, diodes and transformers or switch cores, required in each system. The numbers of components required for the selection of 1 out of N lines, each giving a bi-directional drive, are given in Table 9.1, together with

TABLE 9.1 Total number of major components required for the selection of 1 out of N lines, using various selection methods for bi-directional drive

Type of Selection	Number of switches, each costing A units	Number of diodes, each costing B units	Number of transformers or switch cores, each costing C units	Total cost
Direct	$2N$	$2N$	—	$2N(A+B)$
Combinatorial	$4\sqrt{N}$	$4N$	—	$4\sqrt{N}(A+B\sqrt{N})$
Transformer-Diode	$3\sqrt{N}$	$2N$	N	$\sqrt{N}(3A+2B\sqrt{N}+C\sqrt{N})$
Switch-Core Matrix	$2\sqrt{N}$	—	N	$\sqrt{N}(2A+C\sqrt{N})$

the total cost of the circuits, assuming that a switch costs A units, a diode costs B units and a transformer and switch core each cost C units.

The relative weights which must be attached to A, B and C

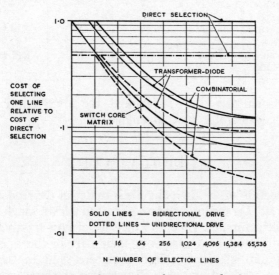

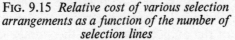

FIG. 9.15 *Relative cost of various selection arrangements as a function of the number of selection lines*

depend on the detailed design of the system, but taking them, for example, in the ratio 15 : 1 : 2 respectively, the selection cost per line, that is, the total cost divided by N, is plotted in Fig. 9.15, as a function of N and relative to the cost per line of direct selection, this latter cost being independent of N. Also plotted in Fig. 9.15 is the cost of selection when the drive need only be uni-directional. Table 9.2 gives the number of major components required in this case. The cost of switch-core matrix selection is the same in both cases and is the lowest for bi-directional drive. However, when

TABLE 9.2   **Total number of major components required for the selection of 1 out of N lines, using various selection methods for uni-directional drive**

Type of Selection	Number of switches, each costing A units	Number of diodes, each costing B units	Number of transformers or switch cores, each costing C units	Total cost
Direct	N	—	—	NA
Combinatorial	$2\sqrt{N}$	N	—	$\sqrt{N}(2A+B\sqrt{N})$
Transformer-Diode	$2\sqrt{N}$	N	N	$\sqrt{N}(2A+B\sqrt{N}+C\sqrt{N})$
Switch-Core Matrix	$2\sqrt{N}$	—	N	$\sqrt{N}(2A+C\sqrt{N})$

uni-directional drive only is required, the combinatorial method shows a considerable cost advantage.

9.2 DIGIT CIRCUITS

The function of the digit circuits is to detect the read-out signal from the storage medium and amplify it to a level which is acceptable to the computer. Except in the case of non-erasable systems, the circuits must also carry out their part in the operation of writing input information into the store, and in the case of destructive read-out systems, of rewriting the previously stored information. Essentially the digit circuit must make a decision, on the basis of the output signal from the storage medium, as to whether the interrogated storage element is storing 1 or 0. This decision always involves discrimination in amplitude and may require discrimination in time as well. Since information which is read destructively must be stored until the rewriting operation is complete, the digit circuits in this case must contain single-bit storage elements. Figure 9.16 is a schematic diagram of the circuits required for each digit in the word, showing all the

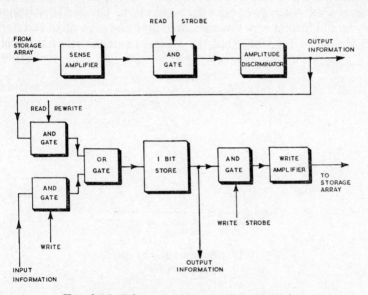

FIG. 9.16 *Schematic diagram of digit circuits*

functions which must be carried out in most destructive read-out systems. These are low-level amplification, time strobing, amplitude discrimination, logic and bit storage and digit write-drive power amplification. In a non-erasable store, only low-level amplification and amplitude discrimination are strictly necessary although time strobing and bit storage may be advantageous. In a non-destructive read-out system, although the rewrite function is unnecessary, the digit circuits must play their part in writing new information.

9.2.1 SENSING CIRCUITS

Of all the functional parts of the digit circuits, the sense amplifier is the most difficult to design with adequate performance.

Since the operation depends on discriminating between the amplitude of the signal representing a stored 1 and the amplitude corresponding to a stored 0, it is essential that the amplifier should provide the necessary gain with a high degree of stability. The threshold of the discriminator, that is, the minimum input signal which causes an output, and the range of uncertainty where the decision about the value of the input signal (0 or 1) cannot be made without some probability of error, determine the input signal level which gives error-free operation. The ideal discriminator would have a very low threshold and no range of uncertainty, as shown in Fig. 9.17, but the typical characteristic has both a

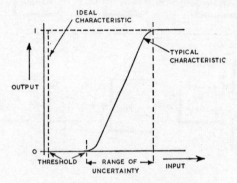

FIG. 9.17 *Characteristic of amplitude discriminator*

high threshold and a fairly wide range of uncertainty as shown. The actual value of the threshold is not so important as the discrimination range, since its absolute value with respect to the signal may be altered by adding or subtracting a constant voltage (or current). At the input to the discriminator the difference between the amplitudes of the minimum 1 and maximum 0, obtained from the array of storage elements, must be several times the range of uncertainty for useful operating margins. This factor determines the gain which must be provided in front of the discriminator. For reliable operation, the amplifier gain must be stable with time and from amplifier to amplifier.

The function of the read strobe is twofold; firstly it renders the sense circuits inoperative except during reading; secondly, in the case of a magnetic-core array with two-coordinate selection, for example, it serves to maximize the 1 to 0 ratio, by eliminating the delta-noise from the signal applied to the discriminator. The delay, which the signal necessarily suffers in the sense amplifier, depends on the gain-bandwidth product of the active elements included in the circuit and on the amount of gain required. The usual formulae[14] for rise-time and bandwidth of an amplifier, consisting of n identical stages, give rise-time proportional, or bandwidth inversely proportional, to $\sqrt{n}$. However, this rise-time figure is the time taken for the output to rise from 10 per cent to 90 per cent of its final value and does not take into account the delay, or time taken for the output to reach 10 per cent of its final value. If the time taken for the output to reach 50 per cent of its final value is taken as a measure of the delay, it is found that this is very nearly proportional to n. For a number of identical circuits in series, each typified by a single time constant given by $1/2\pi f_c$, where f_c is the cut-off frequency of the circuit, the delay, t_d, is given approximately by

$$t_d = \frac{n}{2\pi f_c}$$

If the total gain required is G, the gain of one stage must be $G^{1/n}$. The gain-bandwidth product for an active device, F, may be defined as the frequency at which the device gives unity gain, so that f_c is given by

$$f_c = \frac{F}{G^{1/n}}$$

and the delay in the amplifier is then given by

$$t_d = \frac{nG^{1/n}}{2\pi F}$$

It is interesting to note that the delay is a minimum when the number of stages is equal to $\log_e G$, or the gain of each stage is e (2·718). In practice, the number of stages in the amplifier is limited by economic and other factors. Variation in delay from amplifier to amplifier reduces the accuracy with which the time when the signal-to-noise is maximum can be defined.

The unwanted 'noise' signals appearing on the sense line pose some severe problems in the design of the sense amplifier. In a magnetic-core store, for example, in addition to the delta-noise from disturbed cores during reading, these noise signals include the e.m.f. induced in the sense line by the digit-write current and the voltage excursions, due to capacitive coupling between wires in the core array. This latter effect should, in theory, be a common mode signal, in which both ends of the sense wire move through the same voltage excursion. However, because of the many different paths by which this coupling may take place, both the amplitude and time of occurrence of these signals may vary, resulting in a differential output between the ends of the sense wire. This differential output is much reduced by a suitable choice of threading arrangement for the cores in the array.[15] The common mode signal will be rejected by a differential amplifier which is sensitive only to a difference in signal level between the ends of the sense wire.

Although steps are usually taken to cancel the noise signal due to the digit current, this cancellation can never be perfect and the resulting signal may be several orders of magnitude greater than the read-out signal. Ideally, this noise should be eliminated from the signal before amplification, by putting the read strobe before the input to the sense amplifier. Unfortunately this is impossible in most cases, since the amplitude of the switching transient introduced by the strobe is not negligible relative to the read signal amplitude. The application of the tunnel-diode as a low-level gating and amplitude-discriminating element has been described,[16] for use with a non-destructive read-out core store, but accurately matched pairs of diodes are required. The bias for each circuit must be individually adjusted and control of the ambient temperature to 1°C is necessary for reliable operation. If a.c. couplings are employed in the sense amplifier, recovery effects are introduced after the digit-write noise. These are due to the decay of charges accumulated on coupling capacitors or flux changes in transformer couplings and can never be entirely eliminated. On the other hand, if a direct-coupled amplifier is employed, drift of the reference level with temperature and other operating conditions is a severe embarrassment. Probably the best compromise solution is obtained with the system of Fig. 9.18. In this arrangement, sufficient gain is provided by a direct-coupled amplifier before the read strobe to eliminate the effect of switching transients. After the noise signals have been removed, the remainder of the gain required is provided by an a.c.-coupled amplifier as shown.

Discrimination between the 1 and 0 signals, by the peak amplitude during the read-strobe time, relies on the peak amplitude and its time of occurrence being accurately defined. As has been pointed out previously, variation in amplifier gain does increase the amplitude range, and variation in delay through the amplifier increases the uncertainty of timing. Although the 'peaking-time',

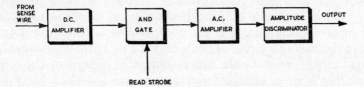

FIG. 9.18 *Sense amplifier arrangement*

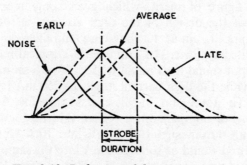

FIG. 9.19 *Reduction of discrimination due to timing uncertainty*

or time when the output from an element storing a 1 is maximum, may be well defined, the limits are bound to be extended by the variation in the amount by which signals are delayed in the storage array. In high-speed systems, this uncertainty of timing can reduce the discrimination by a considerable factor, as illustrated in Fig. 9.19. If the read-strobe timing is set for the mean signal delay, the output, obtained for the earliest or latest signals, is lower. The sensing system may be made less sensitive to variations in timing by integrating the signal during the strobe time and discriminating on the amplitude of this integrated signal rather than the peak-signal amplitude.

9.2.2 WRITING CIRCUITS

The part of the digit circuits associated with writing into the store include the write or rewrite logic, the single-bit storage element and the write amplifier. The bit store is usually a bi-stable circuit and the logic is carried out by conventional techniques as used in digital circuits. Although the output digit may be taken from the amplitude discriminator, through a suitable buffer amplifier, it is present only for the duration of the read strobe and, in most applications, it is more convenient to take the output from the bi-stable circuit. In this case the delay through the extra logic stages increases the access time. The design of the write amplifier is quite straightforward, the main problem being the provision of an accurate digit-write current (or voltage) at the power level required for writing.

A useful figure of merit, which gives some measure of the complexity of the design of the digit circuits, is the total gain required from the input to the sense amplifier to the output from the write amplifier. For example, in a typical magnetic-core store, the input signal level might be 50 mV into an impedance of 100 Ω say, while the digit current might be 250 mA into the same impedance. The total gain, in this case, is therefore $2·5 \times 10^4$ or some 44 db. For comparison, a typical thin magnetic-film store might give an output signal of 2 mV into 10 Ω while the digit current required would be some 500 mA into the same impedance. Here, the total gain required is $6·25 \times 10^6$ or some 68 db. As an indication of how much better the tunnel-diode store is in this respect, the output signal might be 2·5 mA into 40 Ω and the digit-write voltage 0·5 V into 40 Ω, giving a total gain required of 25 or 14 db.

9.2.3 CONTROL CIRCUITS

The form of the control circuits depends very much on the application for which the store is required, but the logical diagram of a typical control unit for a general-purpose destructive read-out system is shown in Fig. 9.20. The operation of this control unit is as follows. If the store is ready to accept a demand for access, or is not 'busy', the flip-flops are all reset (output in the state representing 0) except f_2 which is set (output 1). The 'read' input from the computer sets f_1 and, since f_2 is already set, the output from the 'and' gate starts the read drive and passes into the delay line. Some time later, determined by the duration of the output pulses required, an output from a tapping point on the line resets f_1 and f_2. The read strobe and any other control pulses which may be required are generated by the output from suitable taps on the delay line. When it is permissible to start the write phase, an output from a tap on the delay line sets f_3. If the 'write' pulse has been previously received from the computer, f_4 will be set and the output from the 'and' gate passes into the write delay

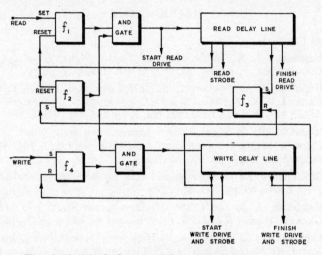

FIG. 9.20 *Block diagram of a general-purpose store control unit*

line. Some time later f_3 and f_4 are reset and the outputs from taps on the line generate the necessary control pulses for the write operation. As soon as it is possible to start another operation an output from the write delay line sets f_2.

The occurrence of a second read pulse while the store is busy sets f_1, but the remainder of the cycle is held up until f_2 is set, indicating that the previous operation is complete. Similarly, if it is desired to introduce a waiting-period between the read and write phase, the latter will not be started until the write pulse sets f_4. An extra input, which is not shown in Fig. 9.20, is necessary to determine whether a rewrite operation is carried out or new information is written. Control outputs from the store to the computer may be derived as required. For example, an output pulse to indicate when the information requested is available and, since it is desirable in most cases to overlap as much of the address decoding operation as possible, an output to indicate when the input address may be changed, will usually both be necessary. In the control of a non-destructive read-out system the read and write control will be separate with interlocks to prevent simultaneous operation, while, for a non-erasable system, only the read-control circuits need be provided.

BIBLIOGRAPHY

ACCESS CIRCUITS

1. Rajchman, J. A. 'Static Magnetic Matrix Memory and Switching Circuits', *R.C.A. Review*, **13**, pp. 183–201 (1952).

2. Robinson, A. A., Newhouse, V. L., Friedman, M. J., Bindon, D. G. and Carter I. P. V. 'A Digital Store Using a Magnetic Core Matrix', *Proc. I.E.E.*, **103**, Part B, Supplement No. 2, pp. 295–301 (1956).

3. Renwick, W. 'A Magnetic-core Matrix Store with Direct Selection Using a Magnetic-core Switch Matrix', *Proc. I.E.E.*, **104**, Part B, Supplement No. 7, pp. 436–44 (1957).

4. Rajchman, J. A. 'Ferrite Aperture Plate for Random Access Memory', *Proc. I.R.E.*, **45**, pp. 325–34 (1957).

5. Rajchman, J. A. and Crane, H. D. 'Current Steering in Magnetic Circuits', *Trans. I.R.E. on Electronic Computers*, EC–6, pp. 21–30 (1957).

6. Lane, A. L. and Turczyn, A. 'A High-speed N-pole, N-position Magnetic Core Matrix Switch', *I.R.E. Convention Record*, 1958, **6**, Part 4, pp. 246–53.

7. Constantine, G. 'A Load-sharing Matrix Switch', *I.B.M. Jour. Research and Development*, **2**, pp. 205–11 (1958).

8. Carter, I. P. V. 'A New Core Switch for Magnetic Matrix Stores and Other Purposes', *Trans. I.R.E. on Electronic Computers*, EC–9, pp. 176–91 (1960).

9. Chien, R. T. 'A Class of Optimal Noiseless Load-sharing Matrix Switches', *I.B.M. Jour. Research and Development*, **4**, pp. 415–17 (1960).

10. Christopherson, W. A. 'Matrix Switch and Drive System for a Low-cost Magnetic Core Memory', *Trans. I.R.E. on Electronic Computers*, EC–10, pp. 238–48 (1961).

11. Minnick, R. C. and Haynes, J. L. 'Magnetic Core Access Switches', *Trans. I.R.E. on Electronic Computers*, EC–11, pp. 352–68 (1962).

12. Neumann, P. G. 'On the Logical Design of Noiseless Load-sharing Matrix Switches', *Trans. I.R.E. on Electronic Computers*, EC–11, pp. 369–74 (1962).

13. Singleton, R. C. 'Load Sharing Core Switches Based on Block Designs', *Trans. I.R.E. on Electronic Computers*, EC–11, pp. 346–52 (1962).

DIGIT CIRCUITS

14. Lewis, I. A. D. and Wells, F. H. *Millimicrosecond Pulse Techniques*, 2nd Edition, Chapter 5. Pergamon Press (London, 1959).

15. Cooke, P. and Dillistone, D. C. 'The Measurement and Reduction of Noise in Coincident-current Core Memories', *Proc. I.E.E.*, **109**, Part B, pp. 383–9 (1962).

16. Perry, G. H. and Shallow, E. W. 'A Read-out Circuit for High-speed Non-destructively Read Stores', *Proc. I.F.I.P. Congress*, 1962, North Holland Publishing Company (Amsterdam, 1963).

17. Goldstick, G. H. and Klein, E. F. 'Design of Memory Sense Amplifiers', *Trans. I.R.E. on Electronic Computers*, **EC-11**, pp. 236–53 (1962).

CHAPTER 10

REVIEW OF CURRENT AND FUTURE DEVELOPMENTS

10.1 REVIEW OF STORAGE SYSTEMS

THE storage systems included in the following survey have been chosen to show the trend of developments in the field. Most of those listed are now in operation although some of historical importance have been included to demonstrate the improvements which have been made since 1950. The erasable stores are considered under the three headings, large capacity, medium capacity and low capacity, while non-erasable systems and those with non-destructive read-out are considered separately.

10.1.1 REVIEW OF LARGE-CAPACITY STORAGE SYSTEMS

Many applications in data processing, and other fields where digital techniques are employed, demand the storage of vast quantities of data. Because the amount of storage required is large, the cost per bit of these systems must be low; for example, the cost of a magnetic-tape system is typically less than 0·01 pence (cents) per bit. All the successful developments in bulk storage are based on the magnetic-surface recording techniques as applied in magnetic tape. Magnetic tape itself offers an economic solution to the problem of large-capacity storage but suffers from the disadvantage that the access time may be of the order of minutes. When the stored items of information can be dealt with sequentially, magnetic tape is an ideal medium, offering the advantages of low cost, high packing density, high data-transfer rates and reliability. Various systems have been developed to reduce the access time, while retaining the advantages of magnetic tape.

180

These include the use of several separate tape loops with a recording and reading head which is moved to the required loop.

Several units, consisting of a stack of flexible or rigid magnetic discs, are now available. Access to the information stored on these discs may be obtained by positioning the heads axially to the selected disc and radially to the selected track. The access time may be further reduced by the provision of individual heads for

TABLE 10.1   Characteristics of large-capacity (greater than 10^7 bits) erasable storage systems

Type of store	Access time in seconds		Capacity 10^7 bits
	Average	Maximum	
1″ Magnetic-tape Unit (3600 ft reel, 1000 bits/inch, 20 tracks, 150 in./sec)	72	288	80
Magnetic-tape Loops (*Burroughs Data file*)	16	48	10
Flexible Discs – single head (*IBM – Ramac*)	0·5	0·8	8
64 Rigid Discs (*Telex Type IIA*)	0·042	0·2	62
24 Rigid Discs (*Bryant Mass Memory*)	0·09	0·167	72
Magnetic Cards – 1 magazine (*NCR – CRAM*)	0·2	—	3·3
Magnetic Cards (*Magnavox– Magnacard*)	—	5·0	60
High-density Drum (*Univac Randex*)	0·385	0·639	1·8
High-density Drum (*ICT – File Drum*)	0·2	0·37	1·5

each disc, thus eliminating axial motion. In other systems the magnetic surface is in the form of cards, which are automatically extracted from storage trays or magazines when required. The necessary relative motion between surface and read-write heads is provided by holding the selected card on a vacuum transport drum which rotates past the read-write station. Refinements in the mechanical design of magnetic drums and the development of high-density recording techniques have made possible file drums with capacities greater than 10^7 bits and access times less than one second. Table 10.1 lists the capacity and access time of some large-capacity systems which are now available.

All the systems listed are erasable stores based on magnetic-surface recording but there are applications for file stores of a non-erasable nature, including, for example, dictionary information in machine translation.

Photographic or optical techniques, with their very high resolution, may be applicable in this field but no system has yet been developed. Photographic techniques are finding present application in several systems for the storage and retrieval of documents.[1,2] The documents are stored as micrographs and are retrieved automatically from the file as required, by means of the file index, which is stored on magnetic discs or cards. Photochromic materials also have been used for document storage[3] and show possibilities for very large-capacity digital storage systems. Photochromic compounds are light-sensitive dyes which exhibit colour changes when exposed to near ultra-violet radiation, so that a pattern, which is transferred optically to the material, is retained indefinitely without further processing. The resolution of such materials is inherently very high, since the changes take place at molecular level; area reductions by a factor of 40,000 have been achieved. Some materials are relatively insensitive to visible radiation and may be read many times before loss of contrast becomes severe.

10.1.1.1 Thermoplastic Recording

Another possible medium for high-density information storage is thermoplastic tape,[4] in which information is recorded as mechanical deformations in the tape surface. The principle is illustrated in Fig. 10.1. The electron beam lays down a charge pattern on the surface of the tape which is then heated to the melting point of the thermoplastic material. The electrostatic forces between these charges and the conducting coating cause a depression of the surface at the points where the charges are deposited. These deformations are frozen into the surface when the tape cools below melting point. Reading is carried out by an optical system which is followed by a television camera tube if an electrical output is required. The system is attractive for television recording but, although the resolution is very high, there are some practical difficulties in the equipment design for digital recording. Firstly, the recording equipment must all be contained in an evacuated enclosure because of the electron beam. Secondly, separate facilities for erasing must be provided; the tape may be

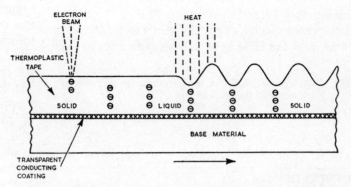

FIG. 10.1 *Principle of recording on thermoplastic tape*

erased by heating up the film to a temperature where the conductivity is high enough to destroy the charge pattern, when surface tension will smooth out the surface. Thirdly, the optical reading arrangements are quite complicated when compared to a magnetic head.

10.1.2   REVIEW OF MEDIUM-CAPACITY SYSTEMS

The main application of storage systems with capacities in the range 10^5 to 10^7 bits is as the internal store for all types of data-processing systems or computers. Acoustic delay lines and electrostatic storage tubes have been employed to provide capacities greater than 10^5 bits but most of the requirements in this class are now filled by the magnetic-drum or magnetic-core store. Except for a very few special applications,[5] the electrostatic tube is now obsolete and has been replaced by magnetic-core storage. For some applications where serial operation is an advantage, acoustic delay lines are still employed. Magnetostrictive delay lines, for example, are suitable for time division multiplexing in electronic telephone exchanges[6] and a few of the smaller computers still use this type of store. The use of magnetic-drum storage is now mainly confined to backing store applications although a few machines still rely on it for the main store. The magnetic drum is an economical form of medium-capacity storage but suffers from the disadvantage of relatively long access time. The choice of drum or core store is governed both by access-time requirements and relative cost.

Several large storage units employing cores have been built,

N

including the TX2, 'S' store at M.I.T., Lincoln Laboratory,[7] which has a capacity of 65,536 words of 37 bits or nearly $2 \cdot 5 \times 10^6$ bits, and the IBM type 738 storage unit, as used in the 704

TABLE 10.2 Characteristics of medium-capacity (between 10^5 and 10^7 bits) erasable storage systems

Type of store	Serial, S or Parallel, P	Average access time 10^{-6} sec.	Cycle time 10^{-6} sec.	Capacity	
				Words	10^5 bits
ACOUSTIC DELAY LINE					
Mercury Delay Lines (*LEO I*)	S	750	—	1024	0·36
Magnetostrictive Delay Lines (*Packard Bell PB250*)	S	1500	—	16,000	3·5
MAGNETIC DRUM					
IBM 650	S	2400	—	4000	1·6
Univac SS80/90	S	1700	—	4000	1·6
Ferranti Atlas	P	6000	—	24,000	12·0
ELECTROSTATIC					
Williams Tube (*Ferranti Mk. I*)	S	400	—	256	0·1
Holding-gun Tube (*M.I.T. Whirlwind*)	P	15	—	1024	0·17
Williams Tube (*IBM 701*)	P	10	—	2048	0·74
MAGNETIC CORE					
2 coordinate (*M.I.T. Whirlwind*)	P	2	9	1024	0·17
2 coordinate (*M.I.T. TX2*)	P	2·8	6·5	65,536	24
2 coordinate (*IBM 7090*)	P	1·0	2·2	16,384	12
2 coordinate (*Plessey – Ferranti Atlas*)	P	0·75	2·0	4096	2
Word organized (*Ampex*)	P	0·9	1·5	8192	4

computer, with a capacity of over 10^6 bits. Although in both these units the store is designed as a single block with only one set of access and digit circuits, the division of the total capacity into more than one block has certain advantages. In addition to a possible decrease in average cycle time (Section 10.3.1), the design problems are reduced and the flexibility of the system is increased since the store may easily be expanded in steps equal to the block size. Because the delays in the system are reduced due to the smaller number of cores in the block, the access time may also be reduced. To make best use of the faster switching ferrites which are now available, the delays in the core array must be kept to a minimum, thus restricting the number of cores which are common to the access and digit circuits. The characteristics of some typical medium-capacity systems are listed in Table 10.2. The comparative cost of these forms of storage cannot easily be established since it must refer to the total system cost. The cost factors relating to any random-access store are discussed later in this chapter in Section 10.4.

10.1.3 Review of Low-Capacity Systems

The main applications for low capacity (less than 10^5 bits) are either as the main store in a low-cost data processor, when cost is the factor determining capacity, or where high-speed operation is required and the maximum capacity is determined by the access time. In applications in the first category storage units are usually similar to those in the medium-capacity class except that here the capacity is tailored to meet the cost requirements. Because the emphasis is on speed in the second category, random access is essential in most applications, although sequential addressing is necessary in some *buffer storage* systems. Wherever information is transferred between two units having differing transfer rates, a buffer store, which is capable of operating in synchronism with either, is essential. For example, buffer stores may be required between auxiliary storage units or input and output devices, and the remainder of the system. The operation of such stores is divided into two distinct phases, namely loading and unloading. In the loading operation, information is written into successive locations; in the unloading operation, the locations are read sequentially and the information transferred to the destination. Thus the operation of a buffer store is quite different from the normal random-access sequence and does not usually require the information to be rewritten even when the read operation is destructive.

Conventional bi-stable circuits may be used for applications requiring high speed and low capacity but are uneconomical for capacities greater than several words. The diode-capacitor store was one of the first types to be developed for these applications. Most high-speed systems in this category are word organized for

TABLE 10.3   Characteristics of high-speed (less than 10 microseconds) low-capacity (less than 10^5 bits) erasable storage systems

Type of Store	Access time 10^{-6} sec	Cycle time 10^{-6} sec	Capacity	
			Words	10^3 bits
Diode Capacitor (*EMI 2400*)	1·5	4·0	64	2·43
2 cores per bit (*Plessey – Ferranti Atlas*)	0·35	0·7	128	3·2
Thin Magnetic Films (*Univac 1107*)	0·3	0·6	128	4·6
Tunnel diode (*Plessey*)	0·075	0·15	64	2·0

maximum operating speed. Two-cores-per-bit techniques have made possible a significant reduction in the cycle time of stores using available ferrite cores. Special cores with more than one aperture have also been used, while the first applications of thin magnetic films are in this class. The tunnel diode has made possible a considerable increase in operating speed over existing stores employing magnetic elements, as will be seen from Table 10.3, where the characteristics of several types of low-capacity, high-speed storage system are listed.

10.1.4   REVIEW OF NON-ERASABLE AND NON-DESTRUCTIVE READ-OUT STORAGE

Where permanent storage of information is required as, for example, in a sub-routine store for a digital computer or in the code translator of an electronic telephone exchange, several techniques have been employed. The most economical systems are those in which the information is permanently wired but, for applications where changing the stored information must be expedited, the inductively or capacitively coupled array, in which information is inserted by means of a punched card, is attractive. For large-capacity requirements, optical techniques are applicable. Since all these systems require only the reading operation, they have, in general, lower cycle times than erasable stores of the same capacity. Although many elements with non-destructive read-out capabilities have been developed, these have not found wide application due to the increased cost of the system. For some

TABLE 10.4 Characteristics of non-erasable storage systems

Type of Store	Cycle time 10^{-6} sec.	Capacity Words	Capacity 10^5 bits
Ferrite Rods (*Ferranti Atlas*)	0·4	8192	4·0
Permanent Magnet Twistor (*Bell Telephone Laboratories*)	5·0	4096	3·6
Permanently Wired Core Matrix (*Edsac II*)	1·5	1024	1·0
Capacitor Matrix (*Bell Telephone Labs.* 'Capstor')	3·0	1024	0·35
Inductive Matrix (*Plessey*)	0·5	4096	2·0
Flying-Spot Optical Store (*Bell Telephone Laboratories*)	2·5	32,768	22·5

special applications, the extra cost may be justified by the advantages obtained. The characteristics of some non-erasable systems are listed in Table 10.4.

10.2 CLASSIFICATION OF ACCESS ARRANGEMENTS

From the description of the various storage mechanisms which has been given in previous chapters, it will be apparent that all the methods of access fall into two categories, *dynamic* or *static* access. In dynamic-access arrangements, there is relative motion between the storage medium and the read-write station. For example, in the cathode-ray-tube electrostatic store, the electron beam which is used for reading and writing is deflected in two dimensions to select the required area of the storage surface. The acoustic delay line uses another form of dynamic access in which the actual medium is not in motion but where the information, in the form of acoustic energy, is moving relative to the medium. Access to all systems employing magnetic-surface recording depend on movement of the storage medium. In static-access arrangements, no motion is involved, the item of information being selected by energizing one or more of a group of selection wires. All truly random-access systems fall into this category, including the Selectron and magnetic-core stores. Indeed a necessary condition for random access is that the access arrangements should be static, since in all dynamic-access arrangements the access time must depend on the address of the required location.

Access arrangements may also be classified by their *dimensionality* or the number of coordinates which must be specified to select one item of information. For example, the cathode-ray-tube store requires movement in two dimensions and hence is a two-dimensional dynamic-access system. A word-organized core store, on the other hand, is a one-dimensional static-access system, while a two-coordinate core store is a two-dimensional static-access arrangement. The Ramac magnetic-disc store is a three-dimensional dynamic-access system, since axial movement takes place to select the required disc, radial motion selects the required track and rotation of the disc is necessary to locate the selected item of information on the track. Systems in which static access is employed in one dimension, while dynamic access is employed in another, are possible. These include, for example, the magnetic drum provided with separate heads for each track, giving a two-dimensional system with static-dynamic access. The magnetic-disc store which has separate heads for each disc is an example of a three-dimensional system with static access to the selected disc and dynamic access to the track and the item on the track.

The cost of dynamic-access arrangements tends to increase with the number of access dimensions while the access time decreases as will be seen from Table 10.1. In the lowest cost system (magnetic tape) the medium moves in one dimension past a single read-write station resulting in a long average access time. The use of two-dimensional access (Datafile tape-loops) reduces the average access time, while this is further reduced when three dimensions are employed (Ramac disc file). By replacing the dynamic arrangement in one dimension by a static-access system (Telex disc file), the access time is again reduced. Although the cost of dynamic-access arrangements, for a given capacity, increases with the number of dimensions, the cost of static-access systems, on the other hand, usually decreases with the number of dimensions. The cost of the latter depends on the cost of the access switch which, in turn, depends on the number of lines which have to be selected. Since, in a one-dimensional system (word-organized), the number of lines is equal to the number of words in the store, such an access arrangement is more expensive than a two-dimensional (two-coordinate) system, in which the number of selection lines is only equal to twice the square root of the number of words. If an n-dimensional static-access arrangement were possible, the number of selection lines would be further reduced to n times the nth root of the number of words. The number of dimensions which can be used with a static-access system depends on the number of terminals possessed by the storage element. For example, any two-terminal device may only be used in a one-dimensional system since one terminal is required for connection to the digit line. All elements which rely on magnetic coupling (for example, magnetic cores and superconductive devices) are not limited in this respect but a practical limit is set to the number of dimensions by the selection ratio. In a three-dimensional access arrangement, the selected element is subjected to a drive of three units, while unselected elements may be subjected to a drive of two units, giving a selection ratio of 3 : 2.

10.3 FACTORS LIMITING CAPACITY

For applications where a large internal storage capacity is desirable, the amount of random-access storage which is provided is usually a compromise between cost and convenience. The user of any system would prefer all the store to be random access and it is therefore worth while to determine the factors which limit the maximum capacity of such systems. Undoubtedly the major limitation is system cost. When one considers that, to manufacture and assemble a store of 10^7 bits in one year, using discrete elements such as magnetic cores, the rate at which the elements must be handled needs to be over 1000 elements per hour, 24 hours a day, an increase of capacity by an order of magnitude is hardly conceivable as an economic proposition. For such capacities, a batch fabrication process, in which the elements are produced at a much higher rate, is essential. The cost of the access circuits for a large store may also be a limiting factor and it is here that the number of dimensions in the access arrangements plays a significant part in determining system cost. For example, a word-organized store with a capacity of one million words requires at least one million selection elements (diodes or switch cores) whose reliability must therefore be of a very high order if the system reliability is to be adequate. On the other hand, in a two-dimensional access system of the same capacity, the number of selection elements is reduced by three orders of magnitude. The factors which determine the cost of a random-access store are discussed in more detail in Section 10.4.

10.3.1 REDUCTION OF EFFECTIVE CYCLE TIME BY DIVISION OF THE STORE INTO BLOCKS

If the total capacity required makes division of the store into several blocks necessary, advantage may be taken of this division to reduce the effective cycle time of the store. For example, when two blocks are required, the addresses of the locations in the store may be interlaced, modulo 2, between the blocks. Thus all words with odd addresses are contained in one block and all with even addresses in the other. If, as is usually the case, locations are referred to sequentially, the effective cycle time will be halved, provided that the access time is not greater than half of the cycle time; this makes it possible for the reading operation in one block to take place simultaneously with the writing operation in the other. When locations are referred to in a random fashion, odd and even addresses occur with equal probability. Thus, there is an equal probability that the next word required will be contained in the same block as the current word or that it will be in the alternate block. In the first case, when the next address is in the same block as the current address, the operation is held up until the end of the current store cycle. In the other case, when the next address is in the alternate block, the writing operation in one block may be overlapped with the reading operation in the other, with a consequent saving of half the cycle time. The average cycle time of the store for randomly occurring addresses is, therefore, 75 per cent of the cycle time of either block.

Four blocks may be interleaved, modulo 4, in a similar way, to reduce the effective cycle time to 25 per cent of the cycle time of one block. Since, in general, the next access cycle cannot be commenced before the item of information, corresponding to the current address, is available, this maximum reduction can only be achieved when the access time is not greater than one-quarter of the cycle time. When the addresses are randomly distributed among the four blocks, there is an equal probability of the delay, before the next word becomes available, being all, three-quarters, one-half or one-quarter of a complete cycle time. The delay is one complete cycle if the next address is in the same block as the current address; it is three-quarters of a cycle if the block containing the next address is the same as that containing the address immediately previous to the current address; it is one-half if the next block is the same as the last but one, and one-quarter of a cycle if the next block has not been referred to during the current and the two previous access operations. The average cycle time for randomly occurring addresses is therefore reduced to 62·5 per cent of the cycle time of any of the four blocks.

In a computing machine each instruction, or operation, requires two accesses to the store, one to extract the instruction and one to extract, or store, the operand. If instructions and operands are stored in two separate blocks, whose operation may be overlapped, the minimum time required to carry out the instruction is reduced to one store cycle time. If the store is divided into four blocks, two storing instructions and the other two storing operands, with addresses interleaved modulo 2 in both sections, the limiting instruction time is determined, in general, by the operand access time since instructions are executed sequentially. For randomly occurring operands, therefore, the minimum instruction time is 75 per cent of the cycle time on average.

10.4 FACTORS RELATING TO SYSTEM COST OF RANDOM-ACCESS STORES

The cost of a complete storage system can be estimated by adding the costs of its main component parts, the storage elements, the access circuits, the digit circuits and the control circuits. Since the control circuits in all storage systems are similar, they can be ignored in a cost comparison, although it should be noted that they may be a significant proportion of the total cost if the capacity is low. Many factors relating to system performance determine the actual cost of the electronic circuits; a very high-speed system requires the latest high-performance components which are likely to be expensive, while a slower system may make use of components which are manufactured in large quantities and are, therefore, comparatively cheap. Two factors on which the cost of the digit circuits depends are, firstly, the gain required in the sense amplifier and, secondly, the digit-write drive power level. The relative costs of the various selection arrangements have been discussed previously and were listed in Tables 9.1 and 9.2.

If P is the cost of one storage element, Q is the cost per word of the access circuits, R is the cost per digit of the digit circuits and S is the cost of the remainder of the system, then in a store consisting of N words, each containing m digits, the total cost of the system is given by

$$\text{system cost} = NmP + NQ + mR + S$$

and the cost per bit is given by

$$\text{cost per bit} = P + \frac{Q}{m} + \frac{R}{N} + \frac{S}{mN}$$

In comparing the costs of different systems, the term in S may be left out, since the cost of the parts of the system which S represents is independent both of the organization of the store and of the type of storage element used. The contribution of the electronic circuits to the system cost is always significant and may be considerably greater than the cost of all the storage elements, especially in those cases where N or m is relatively low. In general, R is a constant for any system but Q depends on the number of words in the store as well as on the type of access system employed. The cost per bit of any store is a decreasing function of the number of words and the relative costs of two systems, with similar access arrangements and the same capacity, depend on the weights attached to P, Q and R. The cost factors for three hypothetical word-organized systems, each with fifty digits in the word and employing combinatorial selection, are listed in Table 10.5. System I may be taken as typical of a magnetic-core store, system II of thin magnetic films and system III of tunnel-diode storage elements. The access costs per word are respectively, for system I, which requires bi-directional drive, $(4A / \sqrt{N} + 4B)$, for system II, which requires uni-directional drive, $(2A / \sqrt{N} + B)$ and for system III, which requires uni-directional drive on two lines, $(4A / \sqrt{N} + 2B)$.

The cost per bit of these three systems is plotted as a function of N in Fig. 10.2, where it will be seen that for capacities below 35 words system III is the cheapest, and above 750 words system

II is the cheapest, while system I is the most economical between these limits.

For a given capacity of N words, each of m bits, with identical storage elements, the relative costs of two systems depend only on the method of selection. The relative costs, in terms of the major components required, of different methods of selection have already been discussed and plotted in Fig. 9.15. The reduction in the cost of the selection circuits when two-coordinate selection is possible is very significant for large capacities. The access costs

TABLE 10.5 Cost factors for three systems whose costs per bit are plotted in Figure 10.2

Cost Factor		Cost		
		System I	System II	System III
Digit circuit,	R	600	900	300
Element,	P	0·5	0·5	10
	A	75	75	50
Access circuit $\{$	B	5	5	3
	Q	$20+\dfrac{300}{\sqrt{N}}$	$5+\dfrac{150}{\sqrt{N}}$	$6+\dfrac{200}{\sqrt{N}}$
Total cost per bit $P+\dfrac{Q}{50}+\dfrac{R}{N}$		$0·9+\dfrac{6}{\sqrt{N}}+\dfrac{600}{N}$	$0·6+\dfrac{3}{\sqrt{N}}+\dfrac{900}{N}$	$10·12+\dfrac{4}{\sqrt{N}}+\dfrac{300}{N}$

of two systems, system IV corresponding to a core store with two-coordinate selection, each coordinate with combinatorial selection, and system V, with thin magnetic films in a word-organized arrangement requiring uni-directional combinatorial selection, are plotted as a function of N in Fig. 10.3. The total access cost of system IV is given by $8N^{\frac{1}{4}}(A + BN^{\frac{1}{4}})$ while the cost of system V is given by $\sqrt{N}(2A + B\sqrt{N})$. The total cost of system IV, when the access costs are taken from Fig. 9.15 and the other cost factors are as given for system III in Table 10.5, is plotted on Fig. 10.2 showing the advantage of two-coordinate selection.

In some cases, the total cost of the electronics for a store with a given capacity may be reduced by choosing the number of digits in a word for minimum cost. This is possible where each item of information is a *character*, often containing six bits representing

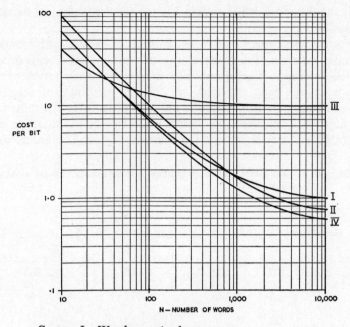

System I—*Word-organized core store*
System II—*Thin magnetic film store*
System III—*Tunnel-diode store*
System IV—*Core store with two-coordinate selection*

FIG. 10.2 *Relative costs of typical storage systems as a function of capacity*

an alphabetic character or decimal digit, and the number of characters in a word is left to the discretion of the designer. In other cases, it may be cheaper to arrange for access to several words in parallel and then to select the required word at the output of the digit circuits. This latter case is particularly applicable to non-erasable stores, where the cost of the digit circuits is low since no rewriting circuits are required. The total cost of the electronic circuits is given by

$$NQ + mR$$

and, where the capacity required is M bits, we have the electronic circuit cost given by

$$QM / m + mR$$

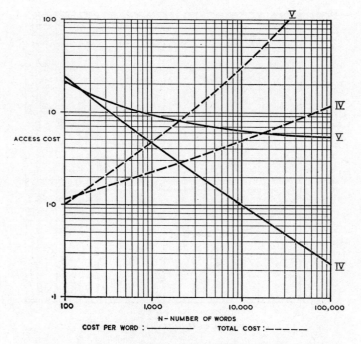

System IV—Two-coordinate combinatorial selection (cores)
System V—Word-organized combinatorial selection (thin magnetic films)

FIG. 10.3 *Relative access-circuit costs as a function of capacity*

This function has a minimum when $QM/m = mR$, that is, when the access and digit circuits make equal contributions to the cost. However, in many cases, Q is itself a function of N and hence of M/m, but it is still possible to minimize the total cost by optimizing m. For example, total circuit costs of two systems, VI and VII, are plotted as a function of m in Fig. 10.4. Both systems are word organized and require uni-directional drive only. Combinatorial selection is employed and the cost factors for both systems are listed in Table 10.6. System VI corresponds to a hypothetical non-erasable system and system VII is the system based on thin magnetic films, which has previously been discussed as system II.

The effect of varying the capacity, M bits, is shown in Fig. 10.4 where the cost of system VI is plotted for three values of M. It will be seen that as the capacity is reduced the optimum value of m decreases.

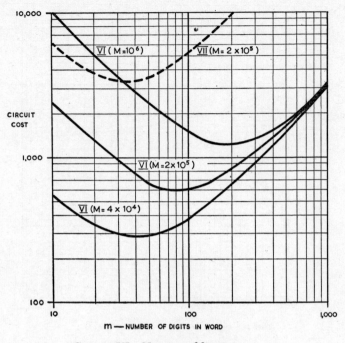

System VI—Non-erasable store
System VII—Thin magnetic film store

FIG. 10.4 *Total circuit costs as a function of number of digits in a word*

TABLE 10.6 Factors in the cost of the electronic circuits for the two systems plotted as a function of *m* in Fig. 10.4

Cost Factor	Cost	
	System VI	*System VII*
Digit circuit, R	3·0	45
Access circuits $\begin{cases} A \\ B \end{cases}$	1·0 0·1	3·75 0·25
$B + \dfrac{2A}{\sqrt{N}} = Q$	$0{\cdot}1 + \dfrac{2}{\sqrt{N}}$	$0{\cdot}25 + \dfrac{7{\cdot}5}{\sqrt{N}}$
Total circuit cost $\dfrac{QM}{m} + mR$	$0{\cdot}1\dfrac{M}{m} + 2\sqrt{\dfrac{M}{m}} + 3m$	$0{\cdot}25\dfrac{M}{m} + 7{\cdot}5\sqrt{\dfrac{M}{m}} + 45m$

10.5 FACTORS LIMITING OPERATING SPEED OF RANDOM-ACCESS STORAGE SYSTEMS

Some of the fundamental factors which limit the access time and cycle time of any random-access store have already been touched upon in sections of Chapter 9. These factors include the

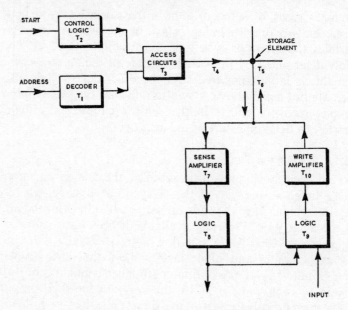

FIG. 10.5 *Sources of delay in typical storage system*

transmission delays in the system and the gain-bandwidth product of the active elements in the access and digit circuits, as well as the switching time of the storage element itself. Shown in Fig. 10.5 are ten possible sources of delay in a typical storage system. These are:

T_1, the delay in the address decoding circuits;

T_2, the delay in the logic circuits in the control through which the start pulse must pass;

T_3, the delay in generating the high-level drive required by the access circuits;

T_4, the transmission delay in the selection circuits and word lines;

T_5, the switching time of the storage element itself;

T_6, the transmission delay in the digit line;

T_7, the delay in the sense amplifier;

T_8, the delay in the logic circuits before the output is available;

T_9, the delay in the logic circuits before writing can commence;

T_{10}, the delay in generating the high-power digit-write pulse.

In many cases, the effect of some of these delays may be masked by one or two overwhelming delays in the system, which then determine the access or cycle time. For example, the cycle time is mainly determined by the switching time of the storage element, when this is large compared with the other delays. Side effects, which are not listed above, may also influence the cycle time. For example, recovery effects in the sensing circuits may make it necessary to delay the start of the next operation.

10.5.1. AMPLIFIER DELAY (T_7)

As has been shown previously, see 9.2.1, the delay in an amplifier may be taken as the sum of the delays in each stage, where the delay in a single stage depends on its gain-bandwidth product, F, and the stage gain. Presently available devices have values of F ranging up to 1000 Mc/s, but this figure is usually reduced by stray capacitances and other factors when the device is wired into a circuit. Taking the optimum amplifier configuration, when the gain of each stage is 2·718, the delay in the digit amplifier circuits may be calculated for the three typical cases following;

(a) a core store requiring a total gain of $2·5 \times 10^4$,

(b) a thin magnetic film system requiring a gain of $6·25 \times 10^6$ and (c) a tunnel-diode store requiring a gain of 25.
With F equal to 1000 Mc/s the delays in the three cases are given by:

(a) 4·4 nanoseconds (10^{-9} sec), (b) 6·8 nanoseconds and (c) 1·4 nanoseconds.

In practice, the number of stages will be limited by economic considerations (in case (b) the optimum amplifier requires 16 stages), so, for comparison, the delays in the three cases, when the stage gain is limited to 30 and the more realistic figure of 250 Mc/s is taken for F, are calculated to be,

(a) 56 nanoseconds,   (b) 72 nanoseconds and

(c) 16 nanoseconds.

10.5.2 LOGIC CIRCUITS (T_2, T_8 and T_9)

Although the number of logic stages, which contribute to the total delay in the system, is small, their effect cannot be neglected in very high-speed systems. Logic circuits, employing tunnel diodes,[8] have been built with a delay of about 2 nanoseconds but these have limited application owing to the two-terminal nature of the device. With the more versatile diode-transistor logic circuit, the minimum delay per stage is about 10 nanoseconds.

10.5.3 TRANSMISSION DELAYS (T_4, T_6)

The transmission delays in the word and digit wires depend on the length of the wires and hence on the capacity and the linear packing density which can be achieved. In a store with a capacity of N words, the length of the digit line is N/p cm, where p is the packing density in bits per cm. The velocity of light in vacuo is some 30 cm per nanosecond hence the minimum digit line transmission delay is $N/30p$ nanoseconds. In practice the presence of insulating and magnetic materials which have a permittivity and permeability, respectively, greater than unity, decreases the propagation velocity. The delay is therefore increased by a factor of 2 or 3.

10.5.4 ADDRESS DECODING CIRCUITS (T_1)

In many applications it is possible to arrange for the address to be available before the end of the previous cycle so that part of the address decoding operation can take place simultaneously with the end of the previous cycle. In a system with switch-core matrix selection, for example, the address can be changed at the beginning of the write phase, since the writing operation takes place when the selected switch core returns to its initial state. With other selection systems, the overlap time available for address decoding is limited to the time which the system needs to recover between cycles. In all combinatorial selection arrangements, in which the decoding takes place at two levels, the first-level decoding is often carried out with conventional diode-transistor logic circuits. The delay in these is usually negligible in comparison with the delay which occurs in the second high-level decoding operation.

O

10.5.5   Access Circuits

The transmission delay in the word-selection lines is minimized for a word-organized system in which the length of the line is confined to the number of elements in one word, m. In a two-coordinate system of N words, the selection lines are common to $m\sqrt{N}$ elements and are therefore considerably longer. The time taken to charge the capacitances of unselected lines, which are connected to the selected line in any combinatorial system, may be a major factor in determining the delay in the access circuits. The corresponding delay in a switch-core matrix is due to the time taken to establish the drive currents in the inductances of the unselected cores on the selected row and column. Both the total capacitance in a combinatorial system and the total inductance in a switch-core matrix are proportional to $\sqrt{N}$.

The control pulses must be amplified from logic level to the power level required to drive the storage elements. Since the gain-bandwidth product of the medium-power elements, which are required in many systems, is considerably lower than that obtainable in low-level amplifying elements, the delay in these drive circuits may make a considerable contribution to the overall delay.

10.5.6   Recovery Effects

Since the operation, which immediately precedes the read phase in a destructive read-out system, is the write phrase of the previous cycle, any effect which delays the recovery of the sensing circuits from the disturbance due to writing may adversely affect the cycle time. Incorrect matching of the sense line may cause reflections (or ringing), which may take some time to decay. By far the major effect is recovery of the sense amplifier, which has already been discussed. The greater the gain required in the digit circuits, the more difficult it is to eliminate these effects. Since the residual disturbance during the read strobe must not be significant with respect to the read signal, the time which must be allowed for any disturbance to decay exponentially to a negligible level increases with the ratio of the amplitude of the disturbance to the signal amplitude. Although the configuration of sense and digit-write lines is arranged to cancel this disturbance, this cancellation can never be exact; the accuracy with which cancellation must be realized for the same recovery time increases with the capacity of the system.

10.5.7 ULTIMATE LIMITS TO OPERATING SPEED

In the light of the above discussion, which has brought out the points where significant delays may be introduced into the system, it is possible to make some estimate of the minimum cycle time likely to be achieved with random-access stores employing discrete elements. The transmission delay in the digit line is one of the most important factors and, either very high packing densities must be achieved, or the capacity will be limited for high-speed operation. The delay in the digit loop depends on the power gain required and may be a very significant factor when the required gain is high. In addition, practical amplifiers will have some recovery effects, which may be significant if the level of the read signal is very low and the write disturbance is not completely eliminated. To illustrate how the access and cycle times depend on these various factors, these times have been plotted in Fig. 10.6 as a function of capacity for three hypothetical systems. The major characterisitics of these systems are given in Table 10.7, the velocity of propagation in the digit line being taken as half the velocity of light.

The characteristics of system I are based on probable developments in ferrite cores, system II is based on the published characteristics of thin magnetic films, while system III is based on what may be achieved with tunnel diodes. It will be seen that the major factor limiting operating speed at high capacities is the transmission delay, which is also shown in Fig. 10.6 for several packing densities. Unless a high packing density can be achieved, therefore, it is impossible to make full use of high switching speeds in large-capacity systems. Shown dotted in Fig. 10.6(b) is the present limit to the cycle times which have been achieved, using either ferrite cores or thin magnetic films.

10.6 FUTURE TRENDS

10.6.1 SYSTEM ORGANIZATION

In recent years there has been considerable theoretical work on the organization of large-capacity file stores.[10] These are of

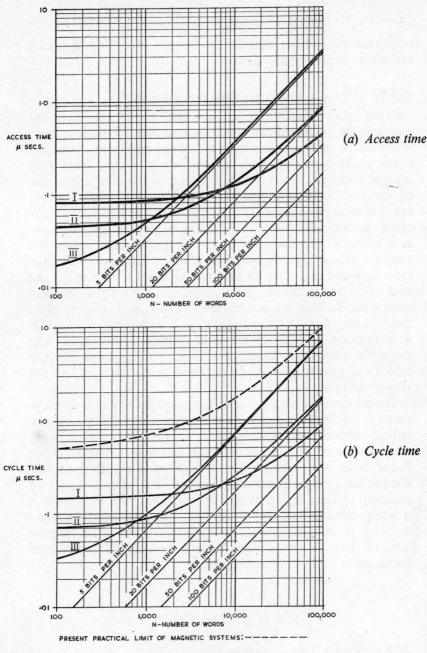

(a) Access time

(b) Cycle time

PRESENT PRACTICAL LIMIT OF MAGNETIC SYSTEMS: — — — —

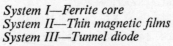

System I—Ferrite core
System II—Thin magnetic films
System III—Tunnel diode

FIG. 10.6 *Limiting operating speeds of typical storage systems as a function of capacity*

TABLE 10.7 Characteristics of the three storage systems whose operating speeds are plotted in Fig. 10.6

Source of Delay		Delay 10^{-9} sec.		
		System I	System II	System III
Control Logic	T_2	6	6	6
Access Circuits	T_3+T_4	$10+\dfrac{\sqrt{N}}{10}$	$10+\dfrac{\sqrt{N}}{20}$	$1\cdot5+\dfrac{\sqrt{N}}{100}$
Switching Time	T_5	50	10	2
Digit-line Transmission	T_6	$\dfrac{N}{300}$	$\dfrac{N}{60}$	$\dfrac{N}{30}$
Sense Amplifier	T_7	14	18	4
Digit Logic	T_8+T_9	9	9	9
Write Amplifier	T_{10}	5	5	$1\cdot5$
Access Time $T_2+T_3+T_4+T_5+T_6+T_7$		$80+\dfrac{\sqrt{N}}{10}+\dfrac{N}{300}$	$44+\dfrac{\sqrt{N}}{20}+\dfrac{N}{120}$	$13\cdot5+\dfrac{\sqrt{N}}{100}+\dfrac{N}{30}$
Cycle Time $T_2+T_3+T_4+2T_5+2T_6+T_7+T_8+T_9+T_{10}$		$144+\dfrac{\sqrt{N}}{10}+\dfrac{N}{150}$	$68+\dfrac{\sqrt{N}}{20}+\dfrac{N}{80}$	$26+\dfrac{\sqrt{N}}{100}+\dfrac{N}{15}$

particular interest in applications involving the retrieval of data from a file where the number of items stored is very large and when the precise location of the item is unknown. The location of the item may therefore involve a search through the entire file and a conventionally addressed random-access store is not ideal for such applications. To meet such requirements the *content-addressed* or *associative* store has been suggested; in this type of store all items would be interrogated simultaneously and the location of words which correspond in whole or in part with the input word would be identified. Since the storage element must be capable of carrying out a logical function as well as storing one binary digit and, in addition, one element per word is required to indicate the location of those words which meet the input specification, such systems are considerably more complex than conventional stores. Several methods of realizing associative stores[11,12] have been proposed, but there are some formidable problems to be solved before the large-capacity systems, which are necessary, become practicable. Systems in which the file is searched sequentially require less equipment and are therefore less costly than those with parallel interrogation but the search time is necessarily increased. Sequential-access systems, such as the magnetic drum, lend themselves to sequential-search arrangements.

Other methods of addressing the stored information, which ease the task of the programmer, are employed in particular applications. These include *indirect* or *relative* addressing in which the address is specified relative to the contents of an index or modifier register, since it is used to modify the address. When items are organized in lists, special facilities may be provided to deal with such cases. For example, instructions are usually carried out sequentially in the order in which they were inserted in the store and a first-in first-out list-addressing system is suitable. For other applications the *push-down* list, in which items are dealt with on the basis of last-in first-out, is advantageous. List-addressing is an extension of relative addressing with special index registers to deal with the lists and both methods may be implemented without special access arrangements in the store.

Because cost often rules out the provision of all the storage required at the highest level, an automatic system has been developed so that a two or more level store appears as a single-level system to the machine user.[13] In this system transfers between the two levels, magnetic cores and magnetic drums, are arranged to take place automatically when required. By extensive use of overlapping techniques in accesses to the core store, which is divided into several independent blocks (Section 10.3.1), the decrease in operating speed is not excessive. The machine is slowed down by a factor of 25 per cent during a drum transfer and the number of transfers required is minimized by a learning programme which ensures that the least useful block of information, or page, is transferred from the core store to the drum, to make way for the requested page from the drum. It is claimed that the convenience and flexibility in the use of the system justify the increase in complexity of the equipment.

10.6.2 STORAGE TECHNIQUES

The history of the electronic digital computer demonstrates the demands made by the user for a continual increase in the capacity of the internal store. In the early computers the capacity provided rarely exceeded 1024 words but now many of the larger systems contain over 100,000 words. Work in many laboratories is aimed at the development of new techniques which may make the production of random-access stores of greatly increased capacity both practical and economic. Batch fabrication of suitable storage elements is an essential requirement and both thin magnetic film and superconductive techniques have this characteristic. Present magnetic film stores suffer from the disadvantage of being word organized which tends to limit their application to more modest capacities. If the claims which have been made on behalf of the continuous superconductive sheet store are substantiated, then a considerable increase in capacity may be possible. There are, however, some formidable problems to be overcome, before their potential is realized.

For the large number of applications where the internal storage capacity need not be very great, the use of superconductive storage, with its attendant need for a liquid helium refrigerator, would be difficult to justify. In this area the choice is always likely to be made on economic grounds and the electronic circuits make a very significant contribution to the overall system cost (Section 10.4). The proven reliability of magnetic core stores, which have been employed in increasing numbers during the past decade, will make their replacement difficult by any unit which does not offer decreased system cost or other substantial advantage.

In addition to the demand for increased capacity, some applications also demand increased operating speed. These two requirements are incompatible in all systems developed so far, since, as capacity increases, operating time necessarily also increases (Section 10.5). Although magnetic films switch very rapidly, other less desirable characteristics of the element make it difficult to achieve very short cycle times. Tunnel-diode stores, although at present relatively expensive, are now approaching the limit which can be achieved with present techniques, at least as far as speed is concerned. If both large capacity and high speed are required, then, unless some fundamentally new concept is discovered, a two-level system must be used. These two levels could consist of tunnel diodes and magnetic cores, for example, or one small fast superconductive store backed up by a large, slower system. To minimize the inconvenience to the programmer, automatic transfer facilities might possibly be incorporated.

For mass, or bulk storage applications, no real competitor to magnetic-surface recording has yet emerged. Recording density is generally limited by the resolution of the reading head and research into alternative reading methods may lead to improvements in packing density and hence to a reduction in access time for the same capacity or an increase in capacity for the same access time. Development of two- or three-dimensional access arrangements will undoubtedly continue with a view to reducing the average access time to the information stored. The extra complexity of the equipment needed to address file information by content militates against the provision of the large capacity which is necessary to make full use of its characteristics.

Information storage has long been recognized as one of the most important functions in a digital computer and, with the extension of digital techniques into many other fields, it has a vital role to play in many other applications. Intensive research and development have led to the great improvements which have been made in the characteristics of storage systems over the past decade. Continued effort is being applied in the search for further improvements. Existing techniques are being refined and extended and alternative methods of storage are being investigated with the aim of meeting the requirements of the computer designer for increased capacity and speed at lower cost.

BIBLIOGRAPHY

1. Porter, R. W. 'A Large-capacity Document Storage and Retrieval System', *Large-Capacity Memory Techniques for Computing Systems*, edited by M. C. Yovits, pp. 351–60, Macmillan and Co. (New York, 1962).

2. Laurent, R. L. 'Combined Magnetic and Graphic Store', *loc. cit.*, pp. 137–48.

3. Carlson, C. O., Grafton, D. A. and Tauber, A. S. 'The Photochromic Microimage Memory', *loc. cit.*, pp. 385–410.

4. Gleen, W. E. 'Thermoplastic Recording', *Jour. Appl. Phys.*, **30**, pp. 1870–3 (1959).

5. Harvey, I. K. 'A Probability Distribution Analyser Utilizing Electrostatic Storage', *Electronic Eng.*, **33**, pp. 432–6 (1961).

6. Flood, J. E. and Simmons, B. D. 'Register Equipment for a Time-Division-Multiplex Electronic Telephone Exchange', *Proc. I.E.E.*, **107**, Part B, Supplement No. 20, pp. 219–27 (1961).

7. Best, R. L. 'Memory Units in the Lincoln TX-2', *Proc. Western Jt. Computer Conference*, Feb. 1957, pp. 160–7.

8. Peil, W. and Marolf, R. 'Computer Circuitry for 500 Mc/s', *Digest of Technical Papers*, Solid-State Circuits Conference, Philadelphia, Feb. 1962, pp. 52 and 53.

9. Rajchman, J. A. 'Computer Memories—Possible Future Developments', *R.C.A. Review*, **23**, pp. 137–57 (1962).

10. Ledley, R. S. 'Organization of Large Memory Systems', *Large-Capacity Memory Techniques for Computing Systems*, edited by M. C. Yovits, pp. 15–41. Macmillan and Co. (New York, 1962).

11. Goldberg, J. and Green, M. W. 'Large Files for Information Retrieval based on Simultaneous Interrogation of All Items', *loc. cit.*, pp. 63–77.

12. McDermid, W. L. and Peterson, H. E. 'A Magnetic Associative Memory System', *I.B.M. Jour. of Research and Development*, **5**, pp. 59–62 (1961).

13. Kilburn, T., Edwards, D. G. B., Lanigan, M. J. and Sumner, F. H. 'One Level Storage System', *Trans. I.R.E. on Electronic Computers*, **EC-11**, pp. 223–35 (1962).

INDEX

209